THE COMPLETE BOOK OF SUBMARINES

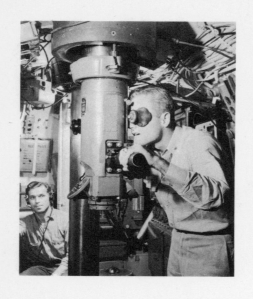

THE COMPLETE

COMMANDER C. W. RUSH, USN,

W. C. CHAMBLISS, AND

H. J. GIMPEL

OOK OF *SUBMARINES*

 CLEVELAND AND NEW YORK

THE WORLD PUBLISHING COMPANY

Published by THE WORLD PUBLISHING COMPANY
2231 West 110th Street, Cleveland 2, Ohio

Published simultaneously in Canada by
Nelson, Foster & Scott Ltd.

Library of Congress Catalog Card Number: 58–9408

60-23343

Contents

THE COMPLETE BOOK OF SUBMARINES

Introduction

ON JANUARY 17, 1955, at Groton, Connecticut, a new era of sea navigation was born. U.S.S. *Nautilus,* first submarine in the world's history, stood out for the open sea.

For over two thousand years mankind had struggled to satisfy an urge to navigate beneath the surface of the ocean. But until *Nautilus* took to the seas, man's efforts had succeeded in producing only a surface ship which could, with varying degrees of success, submerge for relatively brief periods of time.

Nautilus is the first true submarine. Her proper habitat is the vast, dark region beneath the surface of the ocean. Occasionally, she comes to the surface, not to replenish her own expended powers but to yield to the only limiting factor in her subsurface endurance—the physical limitations of man to withstand the environment.

It is true that for over three centuries, the world has known submersible craft which went by the name of submarines. They performed noteworthy service, and in two World Wars brave men on opposing sides went to high adventure and death in these craft. We shall, in deference to the verdict and practice of history, refer to these craft as submarines. But we postulate the reservation that they were so called only because the true submarine, as embodied in *Nautilus,* had not yet been achieved by man.

Nautilus and the other true submarines that follow her may hold the key to the kind of world that will exist in the foreseeable future. They have the ability to operate in virtual secrecy. Submarines can launch at times and places of their own choosing the most modern guided missiles. The nation which boldly adopts the concept of true submarine employment may win the power to determine the way of life of the earth's peoples.

In 1958, Soviet Russia had more undersea craft in commission than all other nations of the world combined.

1. The Submersible Is Born

THE BEGINNINGS of man's probing into the depths beneath the surface of the sea are lost in the period of prehistory. Apparently such investigations had been going on for a long time before the fourth century B.C., because Aristotle reports, without any note of amazement, that Alexander the Great used diving bells to get men beneath the surface as a phase of his siege of Tyre. Herodotus even describes some unsuccessful subsurface excursions over a hundred years earlier.

The development of a craft which could operate under its own power, submerge and ascend at will, navigate with reasonable accuracy and perform a useful mission, was to require a period of more than twenty centuries. Centuries of rejection by those in authority punctuated by brief, grudging gestures of acceptance in the face of desperate necessity—centuries during which there occasionally emerged from the run of ordinary men a few who had the courage to risk unknown peril, the hardihood to ignore or challenge ridicule and opposition, and the dedication to place their lives and their fortunes as offerings on the altar of the undersea gods.

Circumstantial accounts, poorly documented, have come down to us concerning submarine experiments during the first fifteen centuries of the Christian Era. Leonardo da Vinci, for example, is reported to have investigated the possibility of subsurface navigation to the extent of descending in a diving bell similar to that of Alexander the Great. But it was not until 1620 that the first

Alexander the Great descends in a diving bell during the siege of Tyre in the fourth century B.C., *as ornamentally depicted in a thirteenth-century manuscript.*

navigable submarine made its appearance. Cornelius Van Drebel, a Dutch physician, designed and constructed the craft, and James I of England was reportedly its most illustrious passenger. Since the original Van Drebel reports were not preserved, reliance must be placed on accounts written some decades later. And perhaps they should be accepted with the grain of salt that even today is well applied to stories told by submariners.

In any event, here is what Van Drebel was said to have accomplished: He constructed a wooden craft and made it watertight with a covering of greased leather. Propulsive power was supplied by twelve oarsmen. The Van Drebel craft was credited with being able to remain submerged for several hours, and its air supply was assured through tubes supported on the surface of the water by floats. It was more than three centuries and several wars later that a similar "snorkel" system was greeted as a startling innovation when it appeared on German submarines in World War II.

Van Drebel's submersible may have done everything credited to it. James I may actually have taken a ride, although monarchs of that day had enough chances to die early without inviting more. But no shadow of doubt darkens the well-documented accomplishments of that remarkable American inventor,

David Bushnell. His submersible craft played a brief and startling, even if militarily insignificant role in the American Revolution.

Bushnell, a Connecticut Yankee, became interested while a student at Yale in the problem of exploding gunpowder underwater. He solved it—for what ultimate purpose he did not record. But a purpose was handed to him when the British fleet bottled up New York harbor and threatened Washington's hold on the entire region. If, Bushnell reasoned, some powder could be exploded beneath the hulls of the British ships, Washington's problem would be solved. With the genius characteristic of the man, he designed a self-propelled submersible for the purpose of getting his powder charges into position.

Because of many novel design features and because she is in fact the first craft of proven ability to navigate submerged, Bushnell's little boat deserves examination. The hull resembled two tortoise shells joined together, and, appropriately, Bushnell named his craft *Turtle*. The oaken hull was 7½ feet long and 6 feet deep, bound with iron bands.

Turtle was a one-man craft. And that one man was a very busy fellow. His hands and feet managed the controls and provided the propulsive power while his eyes scanned the situation and his mind worked out the tactical problems of approach to the target.

Driven by a screw propeller, *Turtle's* power was supplied by one arm of the talented and husky operator. Steering to right and left was effected by a tiller stuck under the operator's armpit. A vertical screw propeller drove the craft

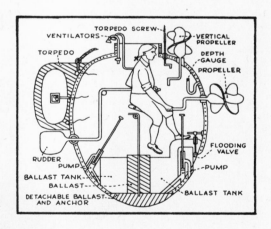

Bushnell's primitive Turtle *was the first submersible to attack an enemy ship.*

up or down to give depth control. It, too, was driven by hand. Which hand? The one on the end of the arm crooked over the steering tiller!

Obviously, it would require continuous cranking of the vertical propeller to keep *Turtle* submerged if some way were not found to balance her buoyancy so that a little thrust would send her up or down. This Bushnell accomplished by fitting his boat with trim tanks which could be flooded to bring the boat to neutral buoyancy. By means of a hand pump the tanks were filled to submerge, and emptied to surface. A foot-pedal arrangement was provided as an alternative to the hand pump—just in case the operator ran out of hands.

One of the main difficulties which faced this ingenious man was the fact that *Turtle's* small hull could contain only about thirty minutes' air supply for the hard-working operator. To minimize this defect, Bushnell installed a rig to assure air being admitted whenever the conning tower was above water. Two pipes—like those credited to Van Drebel's boat—took in fresh air and exhausted foul air. But Bushnell also added a significant refinement: valves on the two pipes closed automatically if water started to enter the hull as a result of wave action or unexpected submergence.

Bushnell knew that accurate information on the depth of the boat beneath the surface was essential for a successful submarine attack, so he invented a depth gauge. It consisted of a glass tube sealed at its upper end and open to the sea at the lower end. A cork floated on the water forced into the tube when *Turtle* descended. Calibration marks etched on the glass tube gave data, and cold light from phosphorescent wood made the gauge readings visible in the darkened conning tower. A magnetic compass illuminated by the same phosphorescent wood kept *Turtle* on course when on the surface or submerged.

Bushnell shared the submariner's traditional desire for a second chance to get back to the surface in case normal procedures failed. He fitted *Turtle* with a detachable keel weighing several hundred pounds. When all was going well, the keel provided stability, and it allowed for emergency reduction of weight if necessary to regain the surface.

Compared with today's complicated undersea craft, Bushnell's *Turtle* was indeed a primitive device. But it represented solutions to the most pressing problems of submergence. Those who followed made improvements in technique but added little to his inspired concept.

After several trials in the Connecticut River, *Turtle* was brought to New York, but ill-health prevented Bushnell from operating the vessel himself. He gave command instead to Sergeant Ezra Lee, a volunteer from a Connecticut regiment of the Continental Army.

Turtle's attack pattern was to approach the target ship, in this case H.M.S. *Eagle,* as closely as possible on the surface, then to descend beneath her hull and heave to. A large wood screw, driven by a crank inside the conning tower, was to be inserted into the victim's hull. Attached to the screw was a line which in turn was secured to the "magazine"—a watertight oaken cask fitted with a time-delay firing device. This weapon contained 150 pounds of gunpowder. Once satisfied that the screw was securely driven into the hull, the operator was to release the magazine. Lighter than water, it would nestle snugly against the hull of the target ship, while the delay-exploder allowed the submariner to get safely away before things blew up.

On the night of September 6, 1776, Sergeant Lee and *Turtle* departed Manhattan Island towed by whaleboats with muffled oars. Nearing the British warships, the boats cast off and Lee was on his own. Here is his own story:

"When I rowed under the stern of the ship I could see men on the deck and hear them talk. I then shut down all doors, sunk down and came up under the bottom of the ship. Up with the screw but found it would not enter. I pulled along to find another place, but deviated a little to one side and immediately rose with great velocity and came above the surface two or three feet between the ship and the daylight, then sunk again like a porpoise. I hove about to try again, but on further thought I gave out, knowing that as soon as it was light the ship's boats would be rowing in all directions, and I thought the best generalship was to retreat as fast as I could, and my compass being no use to me I was obliged to rise up every few minutes to see that I sailed in the right direction.

"While on my passage up to the city my course, owing to the above circumstances, was very crooked and zig-zag and the enemy's attention was drawn towards me from Governor's Island. When I was abreast of the fort on the island, 300 or 400 men got up on the parapet to observe me; at length a number came down to the shore, shoved off in a 12 oar'd barge with 5 or 6 sitters and pulled for me. I eyed them, and when they got within 50 or 60 yards of me I let loose the magazine in hopes that if they should take me they would likewise pick up the magazine, and then we should all be blown up together. But as kind Providence would have it, they took fright and returned to the island to my infinite joy. I then weathered the island and our people seeing me came off in a whale boat and towed me in. The magazine, after getting a little past the island, went off with a tremendous explosion, throwing bodies of water to immense height."

Startled British captains hastily slipped their cables and took their ships to berths farther downstream. But no damage was done. Before another attempt could be made, Washington's forces were driven from Manhattan, and *Turtle* thus lost her only base within striking distance of the enemy fleet. To sail miles down the Hudson was beyond her capability.

Bushnell received neither financial aid nor official encouragement in his work. Years later, Washington referred briefly to Bushnell's invention, commented that it might perhaps have had a touch of genius. Such posthumous recognition, however useless, was better than most submarine pioneers received. Usually they were not only rejected but also promptly forgotten.

A quarter of a century after *Turtle's* adventure, another American, Robert Fulton, brought his brilliant mind to bear on the problem of submarine navigation. Fulton was residing in France in the year 1800. At that time, Napoleon, First Consul of France, was making a good defensive stand against England, but the threat posed by Britain's overwhelming sea power was a serious one. France was in no position to build a fleet to challenge the British. Even if materials and building yards had been available, the country lacked trained sea fighters.

Fulton offered a solution: use a submarine. Capable of attacking without fear of detection, able to plant mines off the entrance to the Channel ports, the submarine could neutralize the surface might of the island Mistress of the Seas. With powerful backers, Fulton secured a grant of 10,000 francs. His first submarine, *Nautilus,* was built near Paris and successfully demonstrated in the Seine.

Nautilus was 21 feet 4 inches long, 7 feet in diameter, and shaped something like a cigar, with the hull being copper-sheathed to reduce skin friction. Flasks holding air compressed at several atmospheres provided replacement oxygen sufficient to permit the boat and her crew of two to remain submerged for five hours.

In June 1801, in demonstrations near Brest, Fulton's *Nautilus* destroyed a sloop in submerged attack. His craft a proven success, Fulton next proposed that he be allowed to attack the British fleet. He asked that he be given a commission in the French Navy, to take him out of the pirate class in the event of capture, and that he be given a reward for each British ship destroyed. There was no quibbling about the reward. But the project fell through on the matter of the commission. The Minister of Marine, Admiral Pleville le Pelley, could not bring himself to issue commissions in his Navy to one "who would employ such methods of destroying the fleets of the enemy."

Fulton dismantled *Nautilus* and departed France for England to try to peddle his idea to the other side. He was received cordially and again given financial assistance to carry out experiments. But in the end, his strange engine of war was sabotaged by the navy he sought to strengthen. Salty old admirals, seeing the doom of ships of the line with their towering masts and billowing canvas, convinced the government that use of a submarine was not a proper British way to fight a war.

Frustrated by conservative naval thinking, Fulton returned to the United States to win lasting fame with his steamboat. But his heart remained with submarines. He was busy on a giant submersible capable of carrying a hundred men when death overtook him in 1815.

Only inconsequential dabbling by theorists marks the history of submarine development during the half century after *Nautilus.* But in 1850 a new name, William Bauer, was added to the roster of zealots who demonstrated the worth and practicability of the submarine only to be balked by bureaucratic resistance to change.

Bauer, a wood turner by trade, built a small submarine at Kiel in 1850. At that time he had more enthusiasm than knowledge, and his boat was not an unqualified success. He did manage to make several dives and successful returns to the surface. But a year after it was built, it went down for the last time with Bauer and two seamen on board.

Unable to bring it up from a depth of 55 feet, Bauer opened the flooding valves to equalize the inside pressure with that of the water outside so that the hatch could be opened. The terrified seamen forcibly stopped that nonsense. But Bauer finally convinced them it was their only chance and with water almost up to their chins, the three were suddenly shot to the surface with a bubble of air that blew the hatch open. Many years later, submariners were to rediscover this simple technique of escape.

Bauer ran out of money and backers in his native Germany, so he went to Austria in search of support. In his year of experimenting with submarines he had apparently become something of a sailor—he managed to interest a lady of charm and influence to back his case! This lovely supporter won Bauer financial assistance from both government and private sources, but as construction was about to start, the admirals got to the Minister of Commerce. That bureaucrat abruptly decided that a submarine was not properly an object of sponsorship by the Austrian Emperor.

The itinerant Bauer left Austria for England. There he gained the favorable attention of Prince Albert, and construction was begun on a Bauer-designed submarine. Unfortunately, local naval architects introduced "improvements" in Bauer's design, and the vessel sank during its first trial run. A lesser man

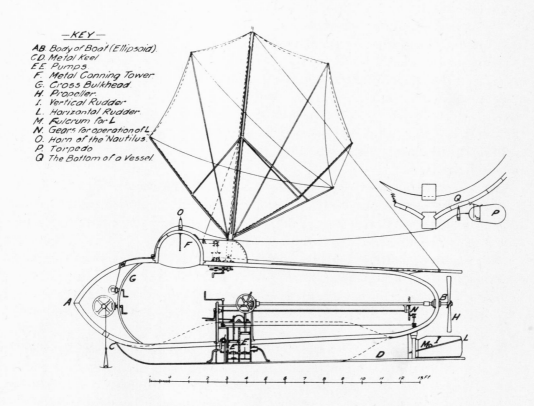

—KEY—
AB. Body of Boat (Ellipsoid).
CD. Metal Keel
EE Pumps
F. Metal Conning Tower
G. Cross Bulkhead
H. Propeller.
I. Vertical Rudder
L. Horizontal Rudder
M. Fulcrum for L
N. Gears for operation of L
O. Horn of the Nautilus
P. Torpedo
Q The Bottom of a Vessel

The first Nautilus. *Designed by Robert Fulton for the French, she was rejected.*

might have been dismayed. But not Bauer. He called at the American Embassy and was politely brushed off. So he went to Russia.

The Russians showed interest in his plans, and Bauer built a new submarine, *Marine Devil,* at Kronstadt. Launched May 28, 1856, she was the largest submersible attempted up to that time, being 52 feet in length, 12 feet wide, and 11 feet deep. Power was provided by a four-man treadmill, which drove a screw propeller. Trim tanks provided for submergence and stability.

Marine Devil demonstrated at her first trials that she could do all the inventor claimed for her, and naturally the old-timers in the Russian Admiralty leaped to battle stations. They required that Bauer prove his craft could pass beneath an anchored ship. He readily agreed. But then the naval authorities anchored the target ship in shallow water. *Marine Devil* stuck fast in the mud. Bauer and his Russian crew narrowly escaped death.

At last the persistent wood turner returned to his lathe.

Russia remained a second-rate naval power.

Seven years later, on the other side of the Atlantic, the Confederate States of America found themselves in the tightening grip of the Union naval blockade. Munitions for the army were cut off. The South could not export the cotton essential to building up foreign credits. The Confederate leaders discovered—too late—that lack of a navy is a fatal weakness to a nation depending for its life on oversea trade.

Lacking facilities to build a navy to challenge the Union fleet in a war to destruction, the South tried various expedients for temporarily breaking the blockade so that fast blockade runners could slip in and out of ports with their desperately needed cargoes. At Charleston, South Carolina, small torpedo boats were built to carry spar torpedoes. Designed to run with only a few inches of hull showing above water, they were intended for night attacks against Union ships in the outer harbor. They never succeeded.

Then, reluctantly and belatedly, the South turned to submarines. The pioneer Confederate submarine builders were Captains J. R. McClintock and H. L. Hunley of the Confederate States Army and a civilian engineer, Mr. Baxter Watson. Early in 1862 the trio built their first submersible at New Orleans. Thirty feet long with a maximum diameter of 10 feet, the craft was constructed of old boiler iron, the only metal available in the South at the time. It was designed for a crew of two, the junior one being selected for brawn rather than brains as it was his job to turn the crank which drove the propeller.

Several test dives were made in Lake Pontchartrain. However, before the craft could be sent into action against the Union fleet under Admiral Farragut, New Orleans was captured and the submarine was scuttled to prevent its being taken by the Union forces.

The three builders escaped capture, however, and made their way to Mobile, where they built another "fish torpedo boat" as they called their submersibles. Practice dives proved this craft capable of carrying out its mission. But while

William Bauer's Marine Devil. *Bureaucratic Russian admirals sabotaged it.*

this submersible was being towed out to make its first attack on a Union ship, a squall blew up and the boat foundered.

Up until this time, Confederate government funds had been made available to build submarines, but after the Mobile failure, that support was cut off. McClintock and Watson had had enough. Hunley persisted, using his personal funds to construct a third submarine. It was to link his name with the first sinking of an enemy ship by submarine action. It was to send him to a sailor's grave.

With the help of Lieutenant J. A. Alexander, an engineer officer, Hunley built a submersible 30 feet long and 4 feet wide. A three-bladed propeller was driven by a crankshaft turned by eight men. To give maximum conceal-ment when running on the surface, the craft was designed with only a few inches of freeboard. Since there was no periscope, the boat was navigated by the cap-tain standing in the forward conning-tower hatch with his head out—a dan-gerous procedure which invited swamping from even moderate waves.

After successful trials in Mobile Bay, the craft was shipped by rail to Charleston where C.S.S. *Hunley,* as she was named, was made ready for action. Her story is one of almost incredible bravery on the part of the succes-sive crews that manned her, of final triumph, and of doom attributable in part to interference from high places.

Of the Union ships blockading Charleston, the most powerful was the steam frigate *New Ironsides*. Boldly this ship patrolled the harbor within easy range of the defending forts, for the shot from the land artillery could not penetrate her armor.

Under command of Lieutenant John Payne and manned by an eager but inexperienced crew enlisted from surface ships, *Hunley* got under way from Fort Johnson to attack *New Ironsides*. Lieutenant Payne conned the boat from the opened forward hatch. A paddle-wheeler, passing close aboard, set up a bow wave. Before Payne could close the hatch, *Hunley* was swamped. Only Payne, who was washed out of the open hatch, was saved.

Undaunted, Payne persuaded the local military command to raise the craft. He encountered no difficulty in mustering a new crew, but early in October 1863 when under way for another try at *New Ironsides,* the submarine capsized near Fort Sumter. Only Lieutenant Payne and one seaman escaped.

That was enough for Payne. He transferred to surface ships, where he served with distinction. But Captain Hunley himself raised a crew of volunteers from Mobile. The salvaged submarine was put in running order once again, and Hunley began a series of indoctrination cruises to train his men. On October 15, the submersible made a routine practice dive under a Confederate warship. She did not reappear.

A week later, *Hunley,* her designer, and her suffocated crew were brought to the surface.

In spite of this series of disasters, Lieutenant Alexander, who had helped build *Hunley,* and Lieutenant G. E. Dixon, another engineer officer, obtained permission from General Beauregard to operate the ill-fated craft once again. After almost four months of intensive training, Dixon, Alexander, and the new crew of volunteers were ready for their attempt. But at this point, a senior staff officer who knew little about submarine operations intervened. He prevailed upon General Beauregard to order the experienced Alexander back to Mobile. Another order directed that the *Hunley* would henceforth operate only on the surface! A new twist in submarine tactics!

Despite these setbacks, Lieutenant Dixon persisted in his efforts.

Shortly after sundown on February 17, 1864, *Hunley* got under way from Fort Sumter for her rendezvous with destiny. The target was the new Union warship U.S.S. *Housatonic*. At her top speed of 4 knots, *Hunley* did not arrive in the vicinity of *Housatonic* until nearly nine o'clock.

The lookouts aboard *Housatonic* at first thought *Hunley's* wake was caused by a school of fish. Only when the submersible was so close that the ship's guns could not be depressed far enough to fire effectively was *Hunley's* identity established. While the crew frantically sought to get *Housatonic* under way, *Hunley* deliberately bored in, her spar torpedo sticking out a few yards ahead of her stem. The torpedo detonated with a terrific roar. *Housatonic* heeled over and sank. *Hunley,* as ordered, was on the surface. The wave resulting from the explosion engulfed the open hatch and she sank close to her victim. The entire crew was lost.

Thus for the first time in history an enemy ship was sunk by a submarine. But it made no change in the prosecution of the war, for it was too late for the Confederacy to adopt the new weapon, build submersibles in number, and train the crews. Such is the pattern of submarine history. The underdog in sea warfare turns to submarines—too late. So, for that matter, does the top dog. But he can better afford the luxury of procrastination, though the cost is always high.

In the three decades following the American Civil War, little took place in submarine development, because no major sea powers were at war. The submarine was related in men's minds to the conduct of war, an association that unfortunately still persists. Its employment in peaceful commerce, which it could advance in efficiency, reliability, and safety, is a field that has yet to be exploited.

But the temporary cessation in the development of the submarine itself was offset by a collateral innovation vital to the ultimate success of undersea warships. In 1868, Robert Whitehead, English manager of an engine factory in Fiume, Austria, perfected the self-propelled torpedo. Such missiles had been tried before, but Whitehead, by inventing automatic controls which kept the torpedo on a steady course at a set depth, provided the weapon which was to make the submarine of the twentieth century a warship of terrible efficiency. With the new weapon the submarine could strike from a distance.

It was in Spain that the next major advance was made toward attainment of a practicable submarine. That nation, once a great sea power, had been forced to accept humiliating insults from a new and powerful entrant in the

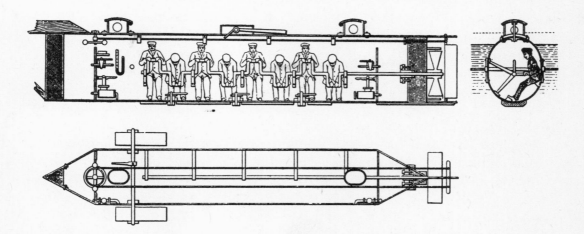

The Confederate Hunley *sank both U.S.S.* Housatonic *and herself with one torpedo.*

naval theater, Germany. To defend his nation's honor, a Spanish naval officer, Lieutenant Isaac Peral, proposed to build a submersible which, he contended, would bring Spain to something like parity with England, Germany, and the United States without bankrupting the national treasury. For two years the Madrid naval bureaucracy studied Peral's plans, guardedly admitted they might have some merit—and did nothing about them.

Finally, in 1887, the navy-minded Queen Regent María Cristina heard about the scheme, and ordered a fund of 600,000 pesetas made available for construction of a submarine. Peral was placed in charge. Although strict secrecy had been enjoined, his progress was widely publicized. In 1889, the submarine was launched.

The Peral submarine was driven by electric motors which derived their power from storage batteries that had to be charged ashore. Their charge was sufficient to give the ship a surface speed of 10 knots, and a submerged speed of 8 knots. Among other advanced features Peral perfected for the boat were an automatic depth keeper, a range finder, compensation magnets for the compass, and a caustic-soda device for removing carbon dioxide from the air.

In its climactic demonstration the Peral submarine fired three Whitehead torpedoes (with dummy heads) at a Spanish cruiser, and scored three hits. That brought to white heat the battle between the Peralistos and the entrenched opposition. Public opinion was on Peral's side, and it looked as though the submariner might win. His success had gained him the stature of a public hero. But, unfortunately, at this juncture Peral made a public appearance in company with the Queen Regent. It was noticeable that he received more and louder applause than Her Majesty. Shortly afterward, a royal commission was convened to study the submarine's performance, and they decided it was a failure.

Seven years later, an American squadron under Admiral Dewey captured Manila and wrested the Philippines from Spanish control. After the war, the Admiral testified before the House Committee on Naval Affairs:

"If they had had two of those things [submarines] in Manila, I never could have held it with the squadron I had."

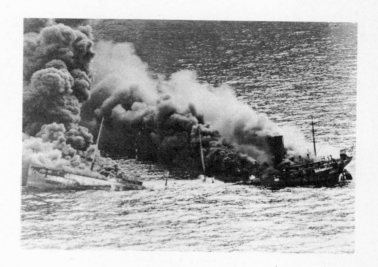

2. Trial by War

AT THE TURN of the twentieth century, the struggle for acceptance of the submarine as a recognized war vessel neared its climax. In the United States, the pressure of Admiral Dewey's testimony strained against the dams of national inertia and naval conservatism. The Navy Department announced specifications for a submarine, and invited bids.

There were two dominating figures in the submarine design picture at that time. One, John Holland, had been experimenting with submersibles for almost a quarter of a century. The other, Simon Lake, had tried his hand in the game for the first time in 1895. Both had constructed craft which would submerge and—very important—would consistently regain the surface.

The Holland and Lake theories of submarine construction differed. Holland conceived of the submarine as a vessel which would submerge by diving beneath the surface with its engine power, in a condition of neutral buoyancy. Lake, however, thought in terms of a craft which would descend on an even keel with a slight negative buoyancy. Lake also saw the submarine as a vehicle which would roam about on the bottom of the sea, provided, of course, the water was not so deep that its pressure would crush the hull. As a result, Lake's first submarine was fitted with wheels. Holland did not conceive of the submarine as a wheeled vehicle at all.

Holland's organization, the Holland Torpedo Boat Company, won the contract for the first Navy submarine and the work was undertaken despite the

John Holland, American submarine pioneer, built the United States Navy's first submarine. In U.S.S. Holland, *conning-tower windows substituted for a periscope.*

fact that Holland himself believed the specifications would not produce a satisfactory boat. He was correct.

The submarine was to have three propellers and the contract required that it be propelled on the surface by a steam engine, and beneath the surface by electric motors. When the ship was put through its first trials, Holland's doubts were promptly vindicated. The time required for extinguishing the fire and venting the steam in the boilers made the period of preparation for diving unacceptably long. In addition, the heat remaining in the firebox after the fire was put out made the interior of the boat unbearably hot when it submerged.

Although the Holland company had spent about $1,000,000 (a lot of money in those days) in research and construction of the craft, for which it was to receive only $150,000, it offered to refund all money advanced on the purchase price. Holland officials told the Navy frankly that the craft would be useless. They asked for the award of a contract to build a submarine for the same price —but to be constructed in accordance with plans and specifications prepared by the veteran John Holland. The offer was accepted. And thus begun an enduring relationship between the Navy and that private company. From then until the present age of nuclear power, Holland's firm—now the Electric Boat Division of General Dynamics Corporation—has been the United States Navy's consistent civilian partner in submarine construction.

The steam-powered monstrosity was scrapped, and the Holland group went to work on a vessel driven by a gasoline engine when surfaced. That plant could be shut down instantly for submergence and transfer to electric drive could be effected with the throw of a switch.

On April 11, 1900, that submarine was accepted by the United States Navy. She was the ninth submersible built by the persistent Holland and she was the first ever to be accepted as a regular element of any navy. Because of her unique place in the annals of naval progress, U.S.S. *Holland,* named in honor of the inventor, merits our examination.

Holland was 53 feet 10 inches long and 10 feet 3 inches in diameter. She displaced a little less than 75 tons submerged.

The gasoline power plant developed 45 horsepower and it served for main propulsion on the surface and also turned the generator for charging the batteries which provided submerged power. The generator, in turn, was so wound that it served as a motor for subsurface operations. This motor developed 50 horsepower.

Holland was also fitted with apparatus which took her automatically to a predetermined depth. The ingenious system consisted of a diaphragm which reacted to outside water pressure. When a preset depth was attained, a mechanical linkage from the diaphragm to the motor controlling the diving planes caused them to level the boat.

A craft as small as *Holland* was sensitive to shifting weights, such as members of the crew walking about, and another device kept the ship in level fore-and-aft trim. This consisted of a pendulum which could be linked to the diving planes when the boat was at desired depth. The pendulum control offset the effects of weight shifts within the craft.

Oddly enough, not even the relatively primitive periscope of that period was fitted to *Holland.* The captain could scan the surface only by bringing the submarine to an awash condition so that he could peer out windows in the low conning tower.

Launching U.S.S. Holland *in 1900.* Holland *marks the beginning of America's undersea fleet, and official recognition of the submarine as a legitimate warship.*

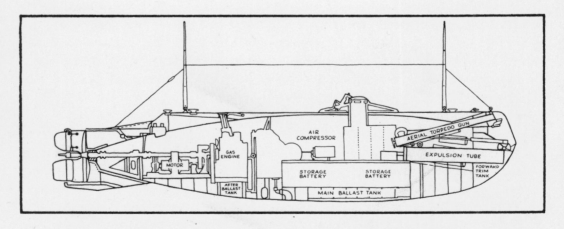

Cross-sectional plan of U.S.S. Holland. *Both gun and torpedo were housed within the hull. A gasoline engine propelled the ship on the surface. Conventional surface-ship design persisted in the form of masts for which a submarine had no use.*

Holland packed a considerable offensive punch. A bow torpedo tube fired an 18-inch Whitehead missile and the boat carried three torpedoes. For surface combat, *Holland* was fitted with a bow gun, recessed into the hull. But its capability was limited for it was aimed by swinging the boat to bear in the direction of the target. There was no provision for changing the angle of elevation and, consequently, chance outweighed marksmanship. There is no record of any hits being scored.

Nevertheless, the Navy was so pleased with *Holland's* performance that it contracted for five more of similar design.

The pioneer gesture of the United States Navy in accepting submarines did not immediately influence other nations. When a question was put in the British House of Commons on news of acceptance of *Holland,* the Parliamentary Secretary for the Admiralty responded: "Admiralty are not prepared to take any steps in regard to the submarine because this vessel is only the weapon of the weaker nation." How rapidly strength could become weakness in face of a submarine onslaught was not to be appreciated until World War I broke out some fourteen years later.

Across the Channel, however, public opinion forced upon staid French officialdom a more progressive attitude. Perhaps there were some who had read of Napoleon's rejection of Fulton and the consequences to the French nation. In any event, some 300,000 francs were raised by public subscription and donated to the government for the purpose of building submarine boats. Construction was commenced.

With that sort of thing happening so close to home, the British Admiralty did a quick about-face. Having no native designers, the government purchased plans from the American, Holland, and started construction of five undersea craft. However, a touch of mystery, not unmixed with suspicion, surrounds those Holland plans. Before emigrating to America, John Holland had lived through the dark days of the potato famine in his native Erin. After coming to the United States, he had designed and built a small war vessel, *Fenian Ram,* which he hoped would be used against the Royal Navy in Ireland's ceaseless struggle for independence from Britain. In short, he did not like England.

When the Holland plans were examined by Captain R. H. S. Bacon, Inspecting Captain of Submarines for the Royal Navy, that officer decided there was something basically wrong. An American naval officer confirmed Bacon's suspicions. Unimpressed by that evidence, however, the Admiralty rejected his recommendation that work be halted until further study could be made. Their Lordships of the Admiralty were convinced only when the first of the five submarines ordered almost turned turtle at its launching.

With Bacon's corrections in the plans, work proceeded on the five submarines. Promptly upon completion, they were ordered to participate in maneuvers with the British Home Fleet. They distinguished themselves by theoretically sinking two battleships which were screened by numerous similar surface vessels. In spite of such successes, however, enthusiasm for the submarine was tempered by apprehension. Britain ruled the seas with the largest, heaviest, mightiest ships afloat. And the most expensive. Could the day be coming when a small submarine, within the price range of relatively poor nations, would challenge the Mistress of the Seas?

In France, the submarine-building program was vigorously prosecuted. It was to place her among the numerical leaders in that category of warship by the time World War I began. But the French Ministry of Marine made one mistake. It rejected a design offered by a French inventor, M. d'Equevilley.

Up to that time, the German Navy had shown complete indifference to the submarine. To the Wilhelmstrasse went d'Equevilley with his plans and he made a convincing presentation. Using his designs, the German Navy built

U-1, first member of Germany's World War I submarine fleet, launched 1906. Not yet considered a formidable weapon, U-1 was viewed skeptically by surface admirals.

U-1, its first *Unterseeboot.* Launched in 1906, *U-1* made scarcely a splash when her small, 101-foot hull hit the water. Displacing only 200 tons, she drew little attention from British eyes dazzled by the impregnable splendor of those unchallengeable sea giants, the Dreadnaught-class battleships.

Two other nations, locked in mortal struggle, looked toward the submarine in urgent speculation. Russia and Japan, both of which had paid no heed to submarine developments, now moved quickly to procure these new tools of sea power. Japan contracted with the Holland Torpedo Boat Company for five submarines. Russia went to Simon Lake, and purchased his submarine, *Protector,* which had been rejected by Congressional vote.

The United States being a neutral, the business of selling belligerent devices such as submarines was not legitimate for its citizens. But submarine builders were, in the nature of the case, an ingenious lot. And business was not so brisk as to allow passing up a sale merely because of somebody's narrow-minded interpretation of the laws of neutrality.

The Holland boats were shipped in parts from Quincy Point, Massachusetts, to Yokohama via Jersey City and Seattle. Simon Lake's *Protector* was a completed vessel when bought by the Russians, but Lake then took her apart and traveled with the parts to Russia to supervise their assembly and to train submarine crews.

Lake built five submarines of the *Protector* design for the Russians. The original boat was shipped by the trans-Siberian railway to Vladivostok to serve as an element in the defense of that key Pacific harbor. But neither the Holland boats nor *Protector* saw action in the Russo-Japanese war. Both sides

Fitted with wheels for travel on the ocean floor, Simon Lake's Protector *was rejected by the United States, but later bought by Russia.*

learned that the mere buying of submarines does not provide a submarine force. Finding the right men and training them effectively can be time-consuming undertakings.

That war was in fact part of a pattern of global restlessness that led inexorably toward the world conflict of 1914. While statesmen uttered pious pronouncements and heads of state exchanged ceremonial messages and visits, naval construction accelerated in the armament race which could not be stayed. But little or no attention was paid to the submarine. Battleships, cruisers, destroyers—those were the types which filled the shipbuilding yards of the great powers.

In 1909, Admiral Sir Percy Scott warned the Admiralty that the submarine would ultimately drive the battleship from the seas. His warning was drowned out in a chorus of ridicule from his fellow admirals. Even in Germany during the eight years between the launching of *U-1* and the outbreak of World War I, only twenty-eight submarines had been constructed. A mere eighteen were fit for distant wartime operations. So oblivious was the German High Command to the potential of the submarine that no thought was given to commerce raiding as a way of starving the British into submission. When the German submarine fleet stood out from home ports in the opening days of World War I, its mission was to operate jointly with the High Seas Fleet against the British Grand Fleet.

In Great Britain only one voice was raised in behalf of the submarine in the opening days of the conflict. Late in 1914, Britain's First Lord of the Admiralty instructed the First Sea Lord to "propose without delay the largest possible programme of submarine boats to be delivered in from twelve to twenty-four months." The author of those words: Winston Churchill.

Churchill was almost alone in recognizing the potential of the submarine. How unaware British captains were of the submarine's capability was graphically and tragically illustrated on September 22, 1914, in the North Sea. In one-two-three order the British cruisers *Aboukir, Hogue,* and *Cressy* were dispatched by a single submarine, *U-9.* Here is how Otto Weddingen, the German U-boat captain, described the event:

"When I first sighted them, they were near enough for torpedo work. But I wanted to make my aim sure, so I went down and in on them. I soon reached what I regarded as a good shooting point. Then I fired one of my torpedoes

Germany's U-9 *sank three British cruisers,* Aboukir, Hogue, *and* Cressy, *in a single engagement during World War I. The lethal potential of the submarine as a weapon of war was thus forcefully illustrated to once-skeptical surface admirals.*

at the middle ship. I climbed to the surface to get a sight through my tube of the effect, and discovered that the shot had gone straight and true, striking the ship, which I later learned was the *Aboukir,* under one of her magazines. There was a fountain of water, a burst of smoke, a flash of fire, and part of the ship rose in the air. She had been broken apart and sank in a few minutes.

"I stayed on top long enough to see the other cruisers turn and steam full speed to their dying sister, whose plight they could not understand.

"I sent a second charge at the nearest of the oncoming vessels, which was the *Hogue.* The attack went true. For twenty minutes the *Hogue* lay wounded and helpless on the surface before she heaved, half turned over and sank.

"When I got within suitable range I sent away my third attack. My crew was aiming like sharpshooters and both torpedoes went to their bulls-eye. The enemy was made useless and at once began sinking by her head."

It seems incredible that two captains, seeing a ship torpedoed, would heave to and make their own vessels sitting ducks for submarine attack. But in September 1914, surface warship captains were too filled with contemptuous ignorance of the submarine to realize that it was a lethal menace. They were to learn the hard way.

By February 1915, the German High Command was forced to admit that the High Seas Fleet had accomplished nothing toward impairing the sea power of Great Britain. It became unmistakably evident that the steady stream of materials flowing from the United States could mean victory for the British. Germany, on the other hand, was facing strangulation from the effects of the British blockade of the Baltic and Scandinavian nations. To the small German submarine force was given the mission at which the surface fleet had failed: blockade of the British Isles.

Under the international rules of sea warfare generally accepted at that time, a blockading warship was required to visit and search a merchant vessel suspected of carrying contraband to an enemy country. That was a doctrine reasonably to be favored by a nation like Great Britain, equipped with an overwhelming surface fleet. But for a submarine, the rule posed certain perils. Under the same rules, there was nothing wrong with disguising a warship as a merchant craft quite capable of destroying any submarine unwary enough to attempt visit and search. German submarine captains soon discovered that to abide by the rules of surface warfare was to invite certain destruction.

On May 7, 1915, *U-20* was on blockade patrol off Old Head of Kinsale on the south coast of Ireland. Mission: intercept vessels carrying contraband to English ports. Shortly before 1:00 P.M., Kapitänleutnant Walther Schwieger sighted a large two-masted ship with four funnels painted the red-and-black of the British-owned Cunard Line. *U-20* submerged. Schwieger estimated that the ship was making 22 knots, over twice the maximum submerged speed of *U-20*. *U-20* was not in torpedo range, and it looked as though the big steamer would get by.

Suddenly, the liner changed course toward *U-20*. Schwieger maneuvered his submarine into position. At 2:09 A.M., he fired one bow torpedo. Range 800 yards. Target broadside to. Sea calm. Conditions perfect. One minute later, the torpedo struck. The speeding steamer shuddered, then began to list to starboard with terrifying rapidity.

Never in the previous history of war had one shot had greater impact on the affairs of the world. The steamer was R.M.S. *Lusitania.*

Among *Lusitania's* passengers were one hundred fifty Americans who had chosen to travel on her in preference to American ships. One hundred twenty-four of those Americans drowned and a wave of horror swept the United States. From Washington went angry protests to Berlin.

Although Germany by this time realized the strategic need for cutting off the war-materials flow from the United States to England, she dared not risk tactics which might draw us in on the side of the British. The German submarine fleet was ordered to cease sinking merchant vessels, even those of enemy countries.

Great Britain speeded up the construction of her own submarine force. And with Britain's merchant fleet free to carry vital supplies across the Atlantic, British and French land forces were able to slow the advance of the German armies on the Continent.

Early in 1916, Grand Admiral von Tirpitz urged the Kaiser to order resumption of unrestricted submarine warfare against the Allies. The Kaiser, still fearful of American intervention, refused to do so. Von Tirpitz resigned. Events demonstrated that von Tirpitz had offered the only plan for German victory. By February 1917, the Kaiser was forced to order unrestricted submarine warfare as the only hope of overcoming Allied strength but the decision was reached too late. The United States entered the war in the spring of that year, and the fate of Germany was sealed.

Although Germany's submarine effort failed due to paucity of numbers and faltering politico-military policy, the record was an impressive one. Over 13,000,000 gross tons of Allied shipping, including three hundred forty-nine British warships, were sent to the bottom. Moreover, the few thousand Germans involved in the submarine campaign tied up over a quarter of a million men in England alone. That was the number Britain was forced to employ in a desperate shipbuilding effort, in manning antisubmarine vessels and in recruiting gun crews for armed merchant vessels.

With the aid of the submarines built in British yards at Churchill's far-sighted orders, the Royal Navy submarine force was able to give a good account of itself. Daring skippers took their boats into the Baltic, disrupting the flow of iron ore from Sweden to Germany. In the Dardanelles operations, so disastrous to British land and surface sea forces, the submarines won outstanding victories. The *E-11,* under the command of Commander M. E. Nasmith, penetrated the Sea of Marmara and sank forty-six enemy ships in one 48-day patrol.

Nearly three years of nonbelligerence had witnessed a great build-up of

United States naval strength from 1914 to 1917. Our battleships, cruisers, and destroyers multiplied in number. And our submarines? We entered World War I with a small force. Only twenty-four were equipped with Diesel engines. Some patrolled the Azores area. Others operated from Bantry Bay, Ireland. There were no confirmed victories for American submarines in twenty-one contacts with the enemy.

France as one of the Allied Powers in World War I presents an anomalous picture. When the submarine became an accepted member of the naval arsenal with the purchase of *Holland* by the United States Navy, France enthusiastically took up the undersea warship. When World War I commenced, she possessed sixty-seven submarines. Of those, forty-nine were completed between 1912 and 1914, giving her the most numerous fleet of modern submarines in the world. But German surface ships seldom put to sea, and there were few suitable targets for French submarines.

On the other side of the world another Allied Power, Japan, showed almost no interest in the submarine. After purchasing five boats from the Holland Company in 1905, she had built only twelve more by 1914. Only two of those displaced more than 500 tons.

As soon as World War I came to an end, our Allies got busy whacking up the spoils. The United States managed to get six German U-boats for the purpose of using them in the Victory Loan drive of 1919. They also served as fruitful objects of study by our submarine designers. But in the wishful-thinking period attending the apparent advent of lasting peace in 1919, the submarine shared the general fate of the United States Navy. Our surface fleet was wrecked by foolhardy disarmament agreements after World War I. The submarine force received its usual share of neglect and between the close of World War I and the commencement of World War II, in 1939, the United States construction program averaged only three submarines a year.

Determined exponents of undersea warfare in Britain, however, succeeded in winning a modest submarine building program. Experimental construction of several types resulted in a decision of major importance made in 1929: the British Navy would standardize on two types of submarines, the S-class and the T-class.

The S-class, 202 feet long and displacing 735 tons, was designed for short-range operations in the North Sea approaches. The T-class, 269 feet long and displacing 1,300 tons, was capable of long-distance operations in the distant reaches of the British Empire. It was fortunate for Britain that, at the outset of World War II, her shipbuilding industry was geared for rapid production of the two standard types.

Germany had been severely restricted by the Versailles Treaty in the size of her military forces. But in 1935, Hitler concluded a naval agreement with the British which permitted Germany to build up to 50 per cent of the submarine strength of Great Britain.

Despite the experience of World War I, however, which had dramatically demonstrated the need for submarines in a battle of the Atlantic, Germany made no serious effort to construct submarines even up to the limits of the 1935 treaty. Admiral Karl Doenitz states that this otherwise incomprehensible omission was due to the fact that Hitler had not contemplated war with Great Britain.

Whatever the explanation, Germany at the opening of World War II presented the classic situation so frustrating to those who appreciated the true worth of the submarine. The German admirals could throw out their bemedaled chests in prideful contemplation of the battleships *Scharnhorst* and *Gneisenau* already in commission, of the giant *Bismarck* and *Tirpitz* consuming tons of precious steel in their huge hulls and towering superstructures. But the thoughtful among them must have felt the cold hand of potential defeat grip their hearts as they viewed the pitifully small force of fifty-seven submarines.

Of those fifty-seven only twenty-two were suitable for operations in the Atlantic sea lanes that were to keep Britain alive on the supplies from overseas. In the first six months of the war, not more than ten German submarines were at sea at one time. On occasion, the number dropped to two.

Germany began World War II adhering to the practice of visiting and searching merchant ships before sinking them and German submarines were forbidden to attack passenger ships. But the installation of guns on British merchant ships and the reappearance of disguised merchant craft as decoys for submarines forced abandonment of that practice. Instead, early in 1940 the German government defined a zone around England within which all merchant ships would be subject to attack without warning. British merchant ships were liable to attack anywhere.

One year of war had demonstrated that Germany must place her fate in the hands of the submariners. The battleships *Tirpitz* and *Bismarck,* and the cruisers *Blücher* and *Prinz Eugen* were completed. But all other major surface ship construction was halted, and the shipbuilding effort devoted to expansion of the U-boat fleet.

Although the undersea fighters of the German Navy were to cost the Allies over 14,000,000 tons of shipping in the North Atlantic, the effort came too late. When the submarine build-up was ordered in 1940, it was realized that the boats thus started could not undertake effective participation in the war until 1942 at the earliest.

In their tactics German submarines had been essentially lone operators prowling for targets of opportunity in the sea approaches to England. But in 1941, Admiral Doenitz established the wolf-pack system. This plan provided that when a U-boat sighted a convoy it reported the position, course, and speed, and then tracked without attacking until additional submarines arrived on the scene to form the pack. Multiple attacks forced the escort warships to divide their defensive effort.

German submarines nesting together under the sign of the swastika.

The toll taken by these wolf packs was enormous.

Meanwhile, the entry of the United States into the war brought about by the Japanese attack on Pearl Harbor had compelled Germany, as Japan's ally, to declare war on the United States. This new development drew the German U-boat fleet to the east coast of North America and for a time the U-boats had a field day. But accelerated antisubmarine warfare by the United States Navy put an end to that.

The development of aircraft radar was undoubtedly a major factor in the defeat of the German U-boat campaign. Naval aircraft operating from the British Isles and Iceland blanketed most of the North Atlantic and the gap between the operating areas of those aircraft was covered by hunter-killer groups. The hunter-killer group consisted of a small aircraft carrier accompanied by destroyers armed with antisubmarine weapons. The far-ranging planes from the carrier spotted submarines on the surface, forced them under and brought the destroyers to the scene.

Soon it became impossible for the U-boats to remain surfaced for vital recharging of batteries and replenishment of fresh air. In the closing days of the war, a German U-boat had only one chance in ten of surviving a war patrol.

Germany lost seven hundred eighty-two submarines in World War II.

In addition to radar, one of the reasons for the increasingly heavy losses sustained by the German submarine forces toward the end of World War II was the slow submerged speed characteristic of all undersea craft of that period. Hunted by planes which brought concentrations of surface antisubmarine vessels to the chase, U-boats could be kept under attack until either sunk or forced to the surface. They were too slow to escape under water.

The Pacific in World War II was the scene of a dramatic demonstration of the capability of the submarine. Our submarines. When the attack on Pearl Harbor all but crippled the offensive striking power of the United States Pacific Fleet surface forces, the Japanese Navy was able to sweep widely in support of Nippon's advancing armies. Malaya and Indonesia were engulfed. Australia was threatened. American surface forces, built around our few aircraft carriers, were hard pressed. They fought bravely and tirelessly but they could, in the main, fight only a defensive, delaying campaign.

From the beginning, American submarines carried the war to the enemy in his own waters. Tactics had caught up with reality by that time, and the submarine was no longer fettered by the antiquated rules of surface warfare which had hampered the German effort in World War I. The initial message to our submarines, from the headquarters of the Chief of Naval Operations on December 7th directed them to "execute unrestricted submarine warfare against Japan." Formal declaration of war did not occur until the next day.

Although the second World War had been in progress for two years, the United States entered the conflict with only one hundred eleven submarines. And of those, twenty-one dated back to the period 1915–1918. Those

Close surface action. The crew of a United States submarine destroys a Japanese trawler with "Molotov cocktails" after damaging her with gunfire.

old-timers were useful only as training craft—and even so employed were none too safe.

At the outbreak of hostilities with Japan, fifty-one American submarines were in the Pacific. Twenty-nine were on the Asiatic station, based at Manila, and twenty-two were operating out of Pearl Harbor. At the end of the war, there were one hundred sixty-nine United States submarines in the Pacific, and in the grueling undersea campaign against the Japanese we had lost fifty-two submarines, aboard them 374 officers and 3,131 enlisted men.

During the Pacific conflict American submarines sank more than 5,600,000 tons of Japanese cargo ships and men-of-war. In addition, about 5,200,000 tons of shipping were damaged. Sixty-three per cent of all enemy shipping sunk by our forces fell victim to the submarines—a branch of the naval service which never exceeded 1.6 per cent of the total United States naval strength in the war. A significant measure of the importance of the work of our submarines can be seen in the fact that our submarines sank slightly over 5,000,000 tons of Japanese cargo shipping, leaving afloat only about 1,000,000 tons. The minimum needed by Japan to sustain civilian life alone was 3,000,000 tons.

But the record of tonnage sunk reflects only a part of the submarine contribution to America's victory at sea. Those remarkable ships and the remarkable men who went down to the sea in them performed all manner of tasks to aid in the defeat of the enemy.

On the other side of the Pacific, in the two decades between the end of World War I and the commencement of World War II, Japan had built some submarines. When the Japanese strategists saw the opportunity which American orientation toward Europe presented in the early years of World War I, increases in the Imperial submarine fleet were undertaken. But the program was not given highest priority. The opening of hostilities against the United States on December 7, 1941, saw a Japanese Navy provided with only thirty modern submarines. An additional eighteen were of almost equal effectiveness although handicapped by the deterioration of age and lack of certain newer equipment. Twelve very old boats, which could be used only for training purposes, completed the Japanese submarine armada—only sixty craft in all.

The fundamental submarine operating policy of the Japanese command at the beginning of World War II tied the submarine to the operations of the surface fleet. The basic strategy demanded the early destruction of Allied naval forces in the Pacific, followed by swift occupation of southeast Asia, Australia, and Indonesia. The element of surprise implicit in the treachery of December 7th was counted upon to make that strategy an overwhelming success. It very nearly did.

Ironically, when the Japanese executed their sneak attack on Pearl Harbor they completely neglected the United States submarine base and directed their attack mainly at the battleships. Our submarine overhaul shops were only slightly damaged. By failing to nullify our submarine servicing capability, the Japanese sowed the seeds of their own defeat, for it was the submarines, operating from Pearl Harbor, that struck back immediately at Japan—one submarine even shot down an attacking Japanese plane at Pearl Harbor. It was our submarines which strangled Japan into submission.

Destruction of Allied commerce carrying men and supplies to the Pacific war theater was a secondary mission for the Japanese submarine force. When, thanks to the survival of our aircraft carriers and submarines in the debacle of Pearl Harbor, Japanese strategy failed to bring overwhelming defeat to the United States Navy, the Japanese submarines were not effectively employed to interdict the flow of arms and men from the mainland of the United States to Pearl Harbor and Australia. That was a fatal mistake.

United States submarines fight back at Japanese air attackers at Pearl Harbor.

Twenty-six submarines of the Japanese Navy were deployed to the Hawaiian Islands in advance of the attack on Pearl Harbor but aside from providing a few bits of reconnaissance information, they accomplished nothing. The fact that they were able to cross the Pacific, however, and maintain for days their stations in the immediate vicinity of America's principal naval and land-based air base in the Pacific demonstrates a capability for undetected operation which neither the bombing aircraft nor the surface naval ship can ever possess. It might be interesting to speculate upon the number of undetected submarines deployed at this moment off the long coasts of the United States.

A desultory attempt to interrupt shipping from Pacific Coast ports of the United States was made after the Pearl Harbor attack. *I-8* operated from San Francisco to Seattle in February 1942, without success. In the same month, *I-17* operated between San Diego and San Francisco. Other submarines on station off our west coast following the Pearl Harbor attack were: *I-26* off Cape Flattery; *I-25* near Cape Disappointment; *I-9* off Cape Blanco; *I-15, I-21, I-23, I-19,* and *I-10* San Francisco and southward. But accelerated antisubmarine measures by United States naval air and surface units soon forced the under-sea craft to withdraw to their base at Kwajalein in the Marshall Islands.

For the rest of World War II, the story of the Japanese submarines is one of too few and too late. Diverted to carry supplies and troops to island areas oc-

The Japanese submarine I-370 *is shown here with a deck load of "human torpedoes."*

cupied by the Japanese, called upon to scout for a fleet growing increasingly fearful of United States carrier task forces, used in futile attempts to sneak raw materials past the United States submarine cordon, the hard-pressed Japanese submarine force was spread thinly and, in the main, futilely, over the broad areas of the Pacific and Indian Oceans.

Japan ordered construction of one hundred fourteen submarines after the attack on Pearl Harbor. But the strangulation of Japanese industry by United States submarines, in addition to the diversion of scarce materials to other purposes, hampered the progress of the program.

By the end of the war, the Japanese had lost one hundred thirty submarines.

Illustrative of the toughness of submarines and the men who sail them is the fact that at war's end, Japan's naval and air forces had been swept from the seas. But fifty submarines were still fighting.

The second World War destroyed the submarine capability of two once-great naval powers, Germany and Japan. In the intervening years, a submarine force larger than any the world has heretofore known has come into being. Soviet Russia, with about five hundred undersea craft in its active fleet, had more submarines in commission in 1958 than all other navies of the world combined.

In that same period, the United States created the most potent undersea fighter ever known—the atomic-powered submarine. Capable of operating indefinitely at the highest speeds ever sustained beneath the seas, able to cruise for months on end without refueling, limited in its submerged endurance only by the physical limitations of its crew, this is the fruition of twenty-two centuries of undersea development—the true submarine.

It will be for historians of a later period to record whether or not our country exploited this great technical advantage in full measure for the security of our people.

In early 1958, the United States had three nuclear-powered submarines in commission and two more were scheduled for commission late in that year. Congress had already authorized a construction program which would give us a total of nineteen by 1961.

The iron-curtain nations were working to match United States attainments in the field of nuclear propulsion. In 1957, Russia announced construction of a nuclear-power icebreaker, but was silent on the subject of nuclear propulsion for submarines.

Japanese fleet submarine returns to harbor after a Pacific war patrol. Ineffectively employed, these submarines never contributed their full potential.

3. *The Driving Force*

THE STORY of the military progress of the submarine is in great measure the story of the development of its means of propulsion. As a surface vessel, the submarine attained propulsive power comparable to other surface ships with the introduction of the Diesel engine in 1912. But the submarine never did attain submerged endurance and speed comparable to surface ships until the dramatic introduction of nuclear power by the United States in *Nautilus,* commissioned in 1954. Then the submarine suddenly attained a range, both surface and submerged, unequaled by any surface ship.

In the beginning, submarines were dependent upon manpower as a source of propulsive effort. Fulton had introduced the sail for surface operations in his *Nautilus* in 1800, but once beneath the surface his boat was propelled by human muscular effort. And although he was the designer of the first successful steamboat, Fulton made no attempt to adapt steam power to submarines for either surface or submerged operations.

The problem confronting submarine power-plant designers was to devise a means of propulsion which did not require large quantities of air. Conventional steam-plant boilers required a constant supply of air for combustion, and presented the added difficulty involved in exhausting the gases generated in the firebox. Human beings too, required oxygen in order to perform work. They could, however, produce more power with less oxygen than any thermomechanical device available during the nineteenth century.

An interesting attempt to find a substitute for human muscles was that of Charles Brun, a French designer, whose submersible *Plongeur* was launched April 16, 1863, at Rochefort. Her motive power was compressed air. The flasks were charged up to a pressure of 12 atmospheres at the pier, and in a trial trip a month after her launching *Plongeur* cruised submerged for a half a mile at an average speed of 5 knots. But the development was not carried forward, another instance of the inexplicable reluctance to accept the submarine as a weapon of war.

The only militarily successful submarine of the nineteenth century, Confederate *Hunley,* was propelled by manpower both on the surface and submerged. And the first officially sponsored United States submarine experiment also involved manpower propulsion. That was the *Intelligent Whale* built under government sponsorship. In 1872 she flooded on her trials, but the crew escaped due to the prudence of its designer in making her fast to a ship by cables prior to conducting the first diving test. That first test was also the last.

An English clergyman, Reverend George William Garrett, made an attempt to solve the problem of submerged mechanical propulsion in 1879. He designed and constructed a submarine, *Resurgam,* propelled by a steam engine. It was planned that the pressure of the steam would be brought to about 150 pounds per square inch just before diving. Then, with the fire doused, the boat would submerge and be propelled by the stored-up steam. It was calculated that the vessel could be propelled about 12 miles submerged. Unfortunately, she sank from other causes before the submerged trials could take place. Seven years later the Swedish gun designer, T. Nordenfeldt, also built a submarine in which stored-up steam was the source of submerged power. But the boat was a failure because of poor stability control.

The Intelligent Whale, *an experimental model. Her first test was also her last.*

Ordered by the United States Navy after the success of the Holland, *U.S.S.* Adder
was gasoline-powered. Diesel engines were not introduced until 1912.

Credit for the first breakthrough of the submerged-power barrier goes to
two English submarine experimenters, A. Campbell and J. Ash. In 1886, they
built a submersible, *Nautilus,* which was powered by a pair of newfangled con-
traptions called electric motors. The motors developed 50 horsepower each,
and were capable of propelling their submersible at a submerged speed of 8
knots with an endurance of about 80 miles. If Campbell and Ash had provided some means of charging the batteries while the boat was under way, they
would have solved the problem, for the electric motor, driven by batteries,
was to be the source of power of all successful submarines until the arrival of
nuclear power. As it was, their *Nautilus* was powered by electric batteries
only, and the boat had to be sure to get some place where the batteries could
be charged before they went dead. As a result, she was not a success.

When John Holland built and discarded the steam-electric submarine first
specified by the United States Navy and substituted the successful gasoline-
electric boat known as U.S.S. *Holland,* he had worked out the first practicable
means of propelling a submarine both on and beneath the surface. His gasoline
engine turned a generator which charged batteries and the batteries provided
current for the main propulsion electric motors.

It was an interim solution only. The gas engine, of similar design to that
employed in the "horseless carriage" of the period, was a temperamental
power plant. In addition, gasoline fumes in the confined spaces of a submarine
hull were an ever-present source of toxic effect upon the crew as well as
potentially a source of fatal explosion.

U.S.S. E-1 *was the first Diesel-propelled United States submarine.*

The gasoline engine was superseded in the United States Navy by the Diesel engine, invented in Germany in the nineteenth century. This was first installed in *E-1,* commissioned in 1912 and it remained the only surface motive power in our fleet submarines until the arrival of nuclear power? Our 1958 fleet of submarines is still overwhelmingly nonnuclear—and will remain so for many years. The submarines of the other free-world nations are conventionally propelled. We shall, therefore, examine the Diesel-electric plant of the fleet submarine of the United States Navy in some detail, as it typifies the propulsion of such a great number of undersea craft.

The chief advantages of the Diesel over the gasoline engine are simplicity, economy, and safety. The Diesel engine has no electric ignition system, its fuel is much less expensive than gasoline, and Diesel oil is also less apt to cause toxic fumes or explosions in the confined spaces of a submarine.

The basis of operation of a Diesel engine, like a gasoline engine, is that fuel and air are burned within its cylinders. This combustion causes the gases to expand at relatively high pressure. The pressure, acting against the engine's pistons, cause them to move and the motion of the piston is transmitted by means of a connecting rod to a crankshaft. The rotation of the crankshaft makes the power generated by the expanding gases available for work.

In the gasoline engine, the fuel-air mixture is made to burn by the action of an electric spark generated by a spark plug in the combustion chamber. To produce that spark at the right instant, in the right intensity, necessitates the employment of a somewhat complex ignition system. In the Diesel engine, however, the ignition of the fuel-air mixture in the cylinder is caused by compression alone. The Diesel cylinder compresses the air and fuel at such great pressure that they ignite without the necessity of a spark.

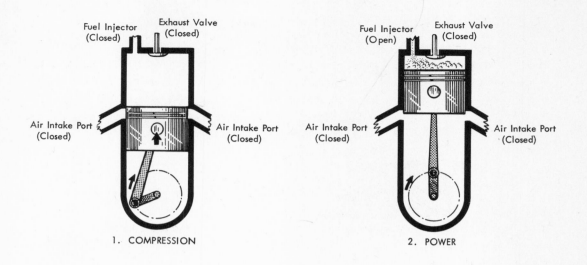

Fuel Injector (Closed) Exhaust Valve (Closed) Air Intake Port (Closed) Air Intake Port (Closed)

1. COMPRESSION

Fuel Injector (Open) Exhaust Valve (Closed) Air Intake Port (Closed) Air Intake Port (Closed)

2. POWER

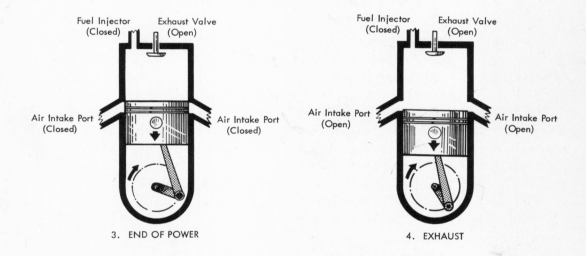

Fuel Injector (Closed) Exhaust Valve (Open) Air Intake Port (Closed) Air Intake Port (Closed)

3. END OF POWER

Fuel Injector (Closed) Exhaust Valve (Open) Air Intake Port (Open) Air Intake Port (Open)

4. EXHAUST

Operation of the two-stroke cycle Diesel engine used in conventional submarines.

1. Compression. The piston moves upward, compressing a charge of air. The air temperature is raised by compression.

2. Power. At top of stroke, fuel is sprayed into cylinder through fuel injector, and ignited by hot compressed air. Burning fuel-oil mixture drives piston downward.

3. End of power. With the piston about halfway down cylinder, exhaust valve opens to release the expanded gases.

4. Exhaust. As piston completes its downward exhaust stroke, the remaining burned gases are driven out through the still-open exhaust valve by the force of fresh air blown through air-intake ports, and the cylinder is refilled with clean air. Compression stage is repeated. Exhaust valve closes and piston travels upward.

The Diesel engines in our submarines are of the 2-stroke cycle type. That means that there is a power-producing combustion of fuel and air once every 2 strokes of the piston. Let's examine the stages by which power is generated in a submarine's 2-stroke-cycle Diesel engine:

1. When the piston is approximately at the extreme distance from the top of the cylinder, a charge of air enters the cylinder.

2. The piston then travels upward, compressing the air. The air becomes very hot, being thus compressed.

3. When the piston is almost at the top of its travel, fuel is injected at high pressure into the cylinder. Striking the hot compressed air in the cylinder, it immediately starts to burn.

4. By the time the burning process has spread throughout the mass of fuel and air, the piston has passed its top position and is ready to start downward. The heat of the burning gases causes them to expand and force the piston downward.

The same action takes place in all cylinders of a Diesel engine. The firing of each is timed to give a continuous series of power strokes so that the crankshaft is always being driven under the power of expanding gases against a piston.

Diesel engines used in our submarines are of two basic designs. The General Motors engines are 16-cylinder affairs, with two banks of 8 cylinders in the V arrangement so familiar in automobile engines. The Fairbanks-Morse engines, on the other hand, are of the "opposed piston" design. They have 10

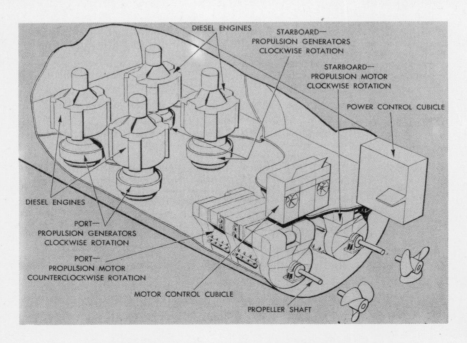

Power-plant layout of the Diesel-electric submarine.

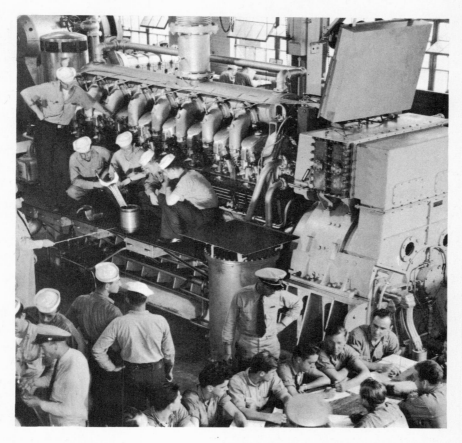

Students studying in the Diesel laboratory of the New London Submarine School.

cylinders arranged in line and in each cylinder there are 2 pistons. The fuel and air are burned by pressure created when the 2 pistons come close to each other near the center of the cylinder.

Each Diesel engine in a fleet-type submarine develops 1,600 horsepower at 750 or 720 revolutions per minute, depending upon which of two standard types are installed. Governors fitted to the engines keep them from overspeeding.

The submarine engineer starts his power plant by the use of compressed air. The air is admitted to the engine through starting air valves and it pushes the pistons in turn and causes them to move. With the engine thus turning over, fuel is injected at the proper instant, and normal combustion takes over the running of the engine.

A fleet submarine has four Diesel engines. These are coupled to four electric generators, which are capable of producing 1,100 kilowatts each. The current from the generators is used to run the submarine's electric motors on the surface, and also to charge the batteries that provide current for the motors when the boat is running submerged.

The main motors which turn the propeller shafts when running both on the surface and submerged are direct-current machines capable of turning over at any desired speed between 40 and 280 revolutions per minute. In earlier submarines, the motors turned over at greater rates of speed, but in order to keep the propeller speed within the lower, more efficient ranges, it was necessary to have reduction gears between the electric motor shafts and the propeller shafts. These gears, even the best of them, were noise producers. In a submarine seeking to slip away from attacking surface ships, silence is golden. To decrease engine noise level, the lower speed electric motors were designed to drive the propeller shafts without any intermediate gear system. The fleet submarine is a twin-screw ship and there are two main propulsion electric motors, one connected to each propeller shaft. Each motor can develop 2,700 horsepower.

As for the batteries in a fleet-type submarine they are of the lead-acid type, just as in an automobile. The positive plate active material is lead oxide and the negative plate active material is sponge lead. The electrolyte is a sulfuric-acid solution.

The submariner has all the battery problems of a car owner—and a few more. He must see that his batteries are kept charged and that the electrolyte level is kept high enough by timely addition of distilled water; these are tasks he shares with the car owner. In addition, however, he must pay very close attention to the battery-gassing problem. All lead-acid batteries liberate hydrogen in both the charge and the discharge process. The car owner doesn't have to give that a second thought, because his battery is ventilated by the outside atmosphere. But it is easy to understand that hydrogen floating around the premises is something to think about in the confined spaces of a submarine.

The safe limit of hydrogen concentration in air is 3 per cent. If it rises to 4 per cent in the submarine battery compartment, it forms an explosive mixture with the air. Hydrogen detectors constantly sample the air, and the concentration is kept within safe limits by ventilation control.

Another battery-gas hazard is chlorine. Chlorine is not normally present, but should salt water get into the batteries, the reaction between the salt and the sulfuric acid forms the highly poisonous gas. Chlorine gas poisoning is thus an added hazard when a submarine is flooded accidentally, and in any flooding the battery compartment is sealed off promptly.

At the beginning of World War II, routine submarine operation required the use of Diesel-driven generators to provide large amounts of current for maximum motor power on the surface. But once submerged, the Diesels could not be used because of their huge demands for air to burn their fuel—24,000 cubic feet of air are required to supply the four Diesel engines for every minute of operation. The motors had to be operated by battery current, a restriction that placed upon the submarine the serious burden of reduced speed and endurance when submerged. For batteries could produce only a fraction of the energy which Diesels could deliver and a fleet submarine capa-

ble of making 20 knots on the surface for thousands of miles could make a
maximum of about 8 knots for one hour when running submerged with only
battery power available.

The vast improvement in antisubmarine capabilities of Allied navies in the
Atlantic caused a sharp rise in the losses inflicted on the U-boats with their
slow submerged speeds. By 1943, U-boat losses rose to nearly 50 per cent of
the total number at sea. In that year, Admiral Karl Doenitz, Commander-in-
Chief U-boats, was made Supreme Commander of the German Navy. Convinced that Germany's only hope of victory lay in her undersea craft, Doenitz
initiated two high priority projects: to produce as quickly as possible a new
U-boat with as much submerged speed and maneuverability as U-boats then
possessed on the surface; and, pending production of the new U-boat, to make
all possible improvements in the capability of the existing craft.

The first innovation was the introduction of the "snorkel" on existing
U-boats. Essentially, the snorkel is a telescoping pipe which can be raised so
as to reach the surface when the submarine is submerged below periscope
depth. Its purpose is to admit air. (Robert Fulton used air intake and exhaust
tubes to the surface in his submarine built in France in 1800.) At once, the
submarine took on a submerged endurance capability comparable to its surface
endurance for it could use its powerful Diesels to provide power while running
beneath the surface. However, the snorkel could not admit enough air for full
Diesel-power operation. Hence, the gain in submerged endurance was not
matched by a gain in submerged speed.

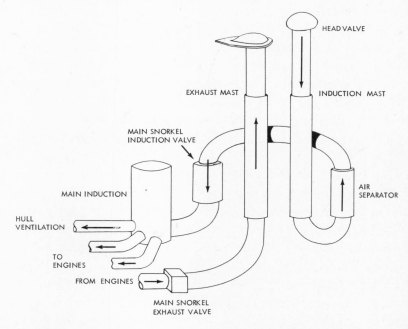

*Diesel-electric snorkel array. Air flows inward through head valve to engines.
Exhaust gases flow from engines through main snorkel exhaust valve to outside.*

Snorkel intake and exhaust heads on World War II German U-boat. The waffle-like rubberized coating is designed to reduce radar detectability of the submarine.

The snorkel was an improvement, and for a time gave the U-boat crews a big boost in morale. But it had a serious weakness—small though the above-surface part was, it could be detected by radar on United States antisubmarine planes flying from the aircraft carriers of the hunter-killer groups. For a long time, German electronics engineers had believed the small snorkel was safe from United States air-borne radar. They lost many submarines before they discovered their error.

German submarine designers, however, recognized that snorkel was a stop-gap solution. In limiting the submerged depth of the submarine to the length of the snorkel pipe, and in forcing the submarine to drag that pipe along through the water, it prevented consistent recourse to the submarine's best refuge—deep diving. Below snorkel depth, the submarine reverted to its old short endurance. One answer which the hard-pressed designers produced was the Type XXI and Type XXIII submarines. In addition to carrying snorkel, these submarines were fitted with batteries of a new design which gave considerably greater submerged power for a longer period than their predecessors. Both could, for moderate distances, outrun their surface attackers. When the first Type XXIII submarines put to sea, seven boats went out and seven came home: quite a change from casualty rates of 50 per cent. Six had made successful attacks.

But again it was the story so familiar in the history of the submarine. The development of the two submarines went into high gear in 1943 when a sub-marine admiral became supreme commander of the German Navy, but research, development, and production do not take place overnight. Those first Type XXIII submarines did not put to sea until March 1945—two months before Germany surrendered. The Type XXI boats never put to sea in time to get into action.

Too few. Too late.

Another attack on the slow underwater speed problem was also initiated in Germany in the closing days of the war. It was the development of the use of hydrogen peroxide as a fuel element in the generation of steam. The idea was originally conceived by the brilliant German scientist, Hellmuth Walter, who now is contributing to the development of rocket propulsion devices for the United States. He proposed its use for submarine propulsion in 1933. Desultory action had been taken at various times, but only in the desperation of looming defeat did the German government push the development of a hydrogen-peroxide submarine engine. The first hydrogen-peroxide boats were ready for operation when the war ended.

Again, too late.

The theory of the use of hydrogen peroxide as a means of developing power was important for the submarine because it presented a means of developing very high power output completely independent of outside air. Hence, the submarine could descend to any depth which it was structurally capable of attaining and still operate at high speed for considerable periods of time.

Hydrogen peroxide is a common chemical. It was for many years a favorite home antiseptic, ready for use whenever little Willie managed to cut himself. Its usefulness as an antiseptic derived from the fact that it broke down chemically in the presence of organic matter. Coming in contact with little Willie's organic tissue, the hydrogen peroxide (H_2O_2) broke down into water and oxygen ($2H_2O_2 \rightarrow 2H_2O + O_2$) and it was the oxygen that performed the task of killing the infectious bacteria in the wound.

Hydrogen peroxide's function in the development of power is to provide the oxygen necessary to combust some other fuel, such as the submarine's Diesel oil.

Here's how it works: Highly concentrated hydrogen peroxide is fed from its stowage tank into a catalyst chamber. The catalytic material in the chamber contains a substance which causes the hydrogen peroxide to decompose into water and oxygen. There are many materials which will perform that function and the permanganates of sodium, potassium, or calcium were used in the Walter engine.

In the process of breaking down chemically, the hydrogen peroxide liberates considerable amounts of heat. The water and oxygen are then led into a combustion chamber where fuel oil is sprayed into the water-oxygen mixture. The fuel oil, combining with the pure oxygen, burns immediately.

The burning fuel oil produces hot gas which, of course, is capable of exert-

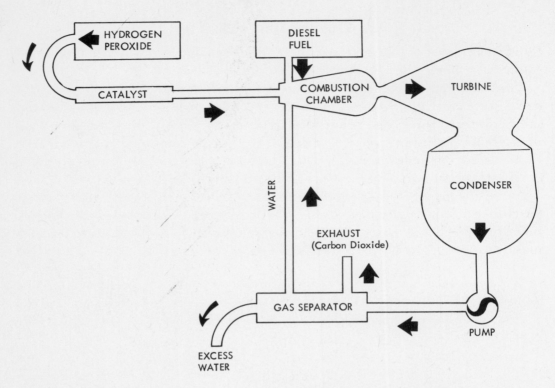

The Walter closed-cycle system. Hydrogen peroxide breaks down in the presence of the catalyst to form oxygen and water. In the combustion chamber, Diesel fuel burns in oxygen, and water forms steam to drive the turbine. Exhaust steam and gas are cooled in the condenser, and after being separated in the gas separator, the exhaust gas is released through vents; water necessary to repeat the cycle is then fed back into the combustion chamber. Excess water is discharged.

ing very high pressure, just as the same fuel burned inside a Diesel-engine cylinder produces the pressure to drive the piston. However, fuel oil burning in pure oxygen develops temperatures much higher than when it burns in air. It is too hot to use in an ordinary engine of any kind and to offset that condition, additional water is sprayed into the combustion chamber. This cools down the gas formed by the burning fuel oil, and at the same time the water thus injected is changed into high-pressure steam.

The steam and burned-oil gases are then led to a conventional turbine. Spinning the turbine, they provide the power for operating the submarine's main propulsion at full speed. Equipped with such an engine the submarine could go as deeply as it wished, at its full surface speed. It could close in swiftly on its victim and be safely away even before the torpedo had struck the target.

In 1945, there was no Allied antisubmarine capability that could have defeated the Walter-engine U-boat. But the Allies did not have to defeat the Walter boats. Germany herself had done so by neglecting for all those years the development of that idea which Dr. Walter proposed in 1933 and which would have made the submarine such a formidable warship.

The future of hydrogen peroxide as a submarine propellant is doubtful. It could have created an important breakthrough in the problem of high-speed submarine operation independent of outside air supply. But the American development of atomic power, which gives the submarine complete freedom from surface air for exceedingly long periods of time while permitting it to cruise at maximum power, is the ultimate solution.

At its inception, the submarine nuclear power plant was an American "exclusive." But experience has shown that non-American scientific experimenting, aided now and then by traitorous transfer of information, tends to make our secrets the property of others before very long.

Still the best means of transferring propulsive effort to the water: the propeller.

4. Anatomy of the Submarine

IN THE EVOLUTION of the submarine, the physical shape of the craft was to undergo as wide a variety of forms as was its propulsion and its tactical employment. Not unexpectedly, the submersible started out in life as an offspring of surface ship design, modified as necessary to permit it to submerge without sinking. Historically, the materials and techniques of submarine hull construction have followed the practices of surface shipbuilding. In the days of wooden ships, for example, submersibles were made of wood as in the case of Bushnell's *Turtle*. The coming of the iron surface warship about the time of the American Civil War saw the advent of the iron submersible, the Confederate *Hunley*. And today, the steel hulls of submarines are of welded construction in conformity with the best practices of ship fabrication. But in matters of design, the submarine presents its own problems.

The *Marine Devil* of William Bauer (1856) showed an insight into the design problem unique in simplicity and validity. Bauer designed his boat to conform as nearly as possible to the contour of a fish, the dolphin, for he postulated the novel theory that since the fish was demonstrably successful in underwater navigation, man could do well to follow the piscatorial pattern until something better came along. His theory had one flaw—it was ahead of its time. The submarine was to remain for ninety-eight years a craft which was essentially a surface ship capable of occasionally submerging.

Then, in 1953, the United States Navy accepted *Albacore*, generally referred to as the world's fastest submarine. *Albacore's* fishlike design was evolved from

54

complex scientific design experiments. Science had discovered nature's wisdom. Time had caught up with William Bauer's vision.

In only one significant feature does *Albacore* depart externally from the smooth contour of nature's submarines. She has a bridge superstructure, a break in ideal streamlining which the submarine designer still accepts as necessary to house periscopes, masts, and the bridge platform. But in *Albacore* even the bridge superstructure is streamlined as much as possible, giving it the characteristics of an oversized dorsal fin.

The refusal to adopt fishlike shapes for nearly a century was not the result of failure to appreciate the advantages of such outlines underwater. It was rather due to the stubborn fact that the submarine was still primarily a surface vessel. When nuclear power made possible prolonged submergence—made the submarine a craft which could spend the greater part of its cruising life beneath rather than on the surface—designers could for the first time think realistically of emulating nature's handiwork. Before the advent of the atomic-driven *Nautilus*, a submarine designed like a fish would for most of its operating time have been in the unhappy predicament of a fish almost out of water.

In the early days of submarine operations, the known phenomenon of water-pressure increase with depth was not a serious factor in submarine design. The chief advantage of submergence was concealment, and as long as the only detecting device directed against the submarine was the human eye scanning from a point of observation no higher than a ship's mast, the requirement of concealment was satisfied by anything which could submerge to a depth of 20 or 30 feet. At 30 feet, the water pressure on a submarine hull is less than 2,000 pounds per square foot.

But the simple picture became complicated with the advent of World War I. The balloon, blimp, and airplane were introduced into the antisubmarine

U.S.S. Albacore's *blimplike shape can be seen by comparing the scale model undergoing wind-tunnel tests with the Navy blimp sailing above the ship herself.*

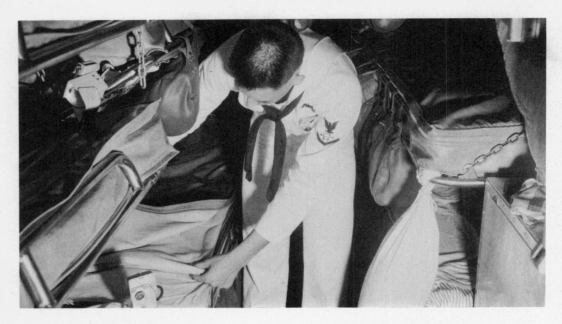

U.S.S. Albacore *is modern in design, but space remains at a premium.*

patrols and observers thus elevated could spot the dark outline of a submarine at considerable depths. In addition, detecting gear on surface ships, based upon the sounds emanating from a submarine operating beneath the surface, replaced the human eye and was far more accurate and sensitive. As the means of spotting the submarine improved, weapons capable of subsurface destruction came into being. And they soon developed into instruments of deadly application.

The submarine was faced with the necessity of going deep if it was to survive.

The answer was to strengthen the pressure hull. Submarine designers are always striving to combine material and design to attain ever greater depth capability. In World War II, for example, a German U-boat was reported to have descended to over 700 feet; at that depth the force exerted against the pressure hull is 44,800 pounds per square foot.

Depth capability information is so important that it must be classified. No government will release current data on that aspect of its submarines' performance, for if an enemy can be sure of the maximum depth at which his opponents undersea craft can operate, he has gone far toward the goal of defeating them. But even classified information sometimes "leaks." During World War II, a blabbermouth gave out the information that our submarines were surviving Japanese depth-charge attacks in the Pacific because they were submerging to depths greater than those for which the Nipponese were setting their charges. With the information thus so kindly provided by a man who did not himself venture into the war zone, the Japanese quickly corrected their attack procedure. The grim notation "missing and presumed dead" was entered with shockingly increased frequency after the names of American submariners.

Inside the all-important pressure hull are the men, the machines, and the weapons which make the submarine a mobile fighting ship. But almost com-

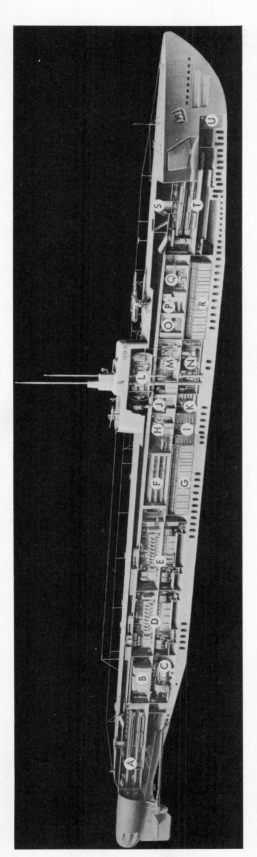

Cutaway view of fleet-type submarine. A, *After torpedo room.* B, *Maneuvering room.* C, *Motor room.* D, *After engine room.* E, *Forward engine room.* F, *Crew's quarters.* G, *After battery space.* H, *Crew's mess and galley.* I, *Magazine.* J, *Radio room.* K, *Storeroom.* L, *Conning tower.* M, *Control room.* N, *Pump room.* O, *Chief petty officers' stateroom.* P, *Officers' stateroom.* Q, *Wardroom.* R, *Forward battery space.* S, *Escape trunk.* T, *Forward torpedo room.* U, *Chain locker.*

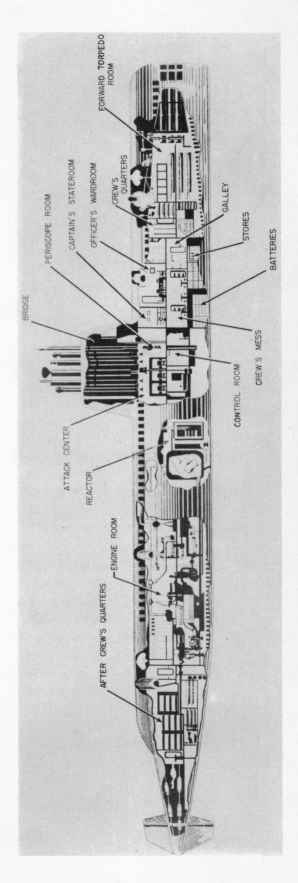

Cutaway view of nuclear-powered submarine.

Outer hull and pressure hull construction of German World War II submarines.

pletely surrounding the pressure hull, and extending for most of its length, is the outer hull. This hull is not subjected to sea pressure when the boat is submerged, for the outer hull is made up of tanks of various sorts which are open to the sea at their bases, and are always full of air, water, or fuel oil whose pressure is equal to sea pressure. It is these tanks which play a vital role in the control of the submarine's buoyancy, trim, and stability.

It would be a good idea to become acquainted at this point with a few technical terms that help in understanding how the designer provides his ship with the capability of submerging and keeping itself in good trim under the water.

First, there is *buoyancy.* That is the upward force exerted against a floating or immersed body by the liquid which the body displaces. The submariner deals with three kinds of buoyancy.

Positive buoyancy is the condition in which a body floats on the surface of a liquid. It exists when the weight of the body is less than the weight of liquid of the same volume.

Neutral buoyancy is the condition in which a submerged body will remain suspended at any given depth in a liquid unless affected by some force, such as the power of its motors in the case of a submarine. It exists when the weight of the body exactly equals the weight of liquid of equivalent volume.

Negative buoyancy is the condition in which a body sinks in a liquid. It exists when the weight of the body is greater than the weight of liquid of an equivalent volume.

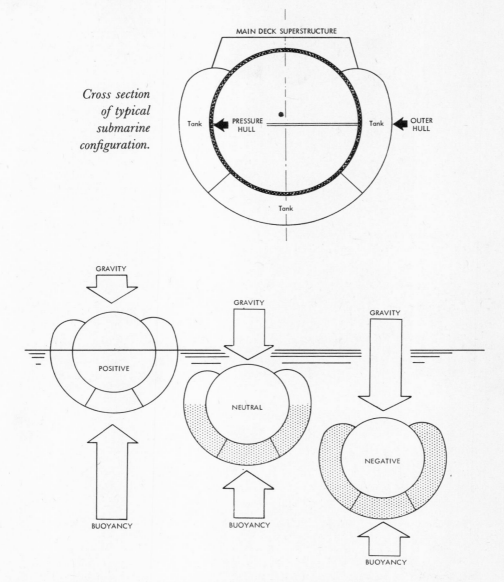

Cross section of typical submarine configuration.

MAIN DECK SUPERSTRUCTURE

Tank   PRESSURE HULL   Tank   OUTER HULL

Tank

GRAVITY

GRAVITY

GRAVITY

POSITIVE

NEUTRAL

NEGATIVE

BUOYANCY

BUOYANCY

BUOYANCY

Submarine buoyancy. The two opposing forces operating on a submarine are gravity, which tends to sink the submarine, and buoyancy, which tends to float it. Relative volume of water or air in the ballast tanks determines which force is greater.

When the submarine captain wants his ship to float on the surface, he arranges matters so that the craft is in a state of *positive buoyancy*. When he wants to submerge he and his crew produce a condition of *negative buoyancy*. And when they want the ship to stay put in a state of suspension, they set up for *neutral buoyancy*.

Naturally, no one would want his ship to remain very long in a state of negative buoyancy, because such a condition means that the ship would keep going down deeper of its own accord. Hence, a submarine is set for negative buoyancy only at the start of submergence. With the dive once started, the craft is brought to a condition of neutral buoyancy so that its depth can be controlled by motors and diving controls.

Now, about this time you may well ask how the submarine crew can blithely change the weight of the ship at will so as to produce any of the three states of buoyancy. It is all done with water tanks, which by the use of pumps or air pressure may be filled or emptied at will.

The tanks with which we are concerned in the process of buoyancy control are divided into three classes: *special ballast tanks, variable ballast tanks,* and *main ballast tanks.*

SPECIAL BALLAST TANKS

Located in the bow of the ship is the *bow buoyancy tank.* It is flooded at the start of the diving operation. When the submarine is submerged, blowing the bow buoyancy tank will give the ship an up angle.

Forward of amidships is the *negative tank.* When all other tanks are flooded so as to create neutral buoyancy, flooding the negative tank will produce negative buoyancy.

Amidships is the *safety tank.* The weight of the water it contains provides sufficient ballast to offset the effect of accidental flooding of the conning tower. It is built to be emptied either by pumps or air pressure, and by being emptied could under normal conditions give the submarine neutral or slightly positive buoyancy.

VARIABLE BALLAST TANKS

Located inside the pressure hull, one near the bow and the other near the stern, are the *trim tanks.* By controlling the weight of water in those tanks, the submarine captain keeps his boat from riding bow-down or bow-up.

Near the center of the ship are two *auxiliary tanks.* The controlled weight of water in those tanks adjusts buoyancy without affecting fore-and-aft trim. They also may be used to control listing to one side or the other.

Almost surrounding the torpedo tubes are *water round torpedo tanks.* These tanks have an important function in the torpedo firing operation. They furnish water for flooding the torpedo tubes in preparation for firing, and receive water drained from the tubes to permit reloading.

MAIN BALLAST TANKS

These large tanks—in a 1,500-ton submarine they have a capacity of 383 tons of water—are flooded only when the submarine is submerged. They are located between the pressure hull and the outer hull and are always open to the sea at the bottom by means of holes called *floods.* Water is admitted by opening *vents* at the tops of the tanks to permit the escape of air forced out by the pressure of sea water.

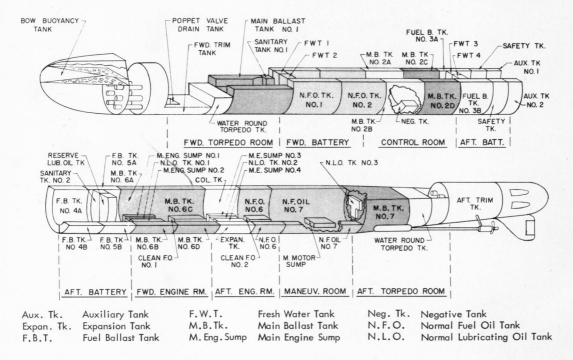

Aux. Tk.	Auxiliary Tank	
Expan. Tk.	Expansion Tank	
F.B.T.	Fuel Ballast Tank	

F.W.T. Fresh Water Tank
M.B.Tk. Main Ballast Tank
M. Eng. Sump Main Engine Sump

Neg. Tk. Negative Tank
N.F.O. Normal Fuel Oil Tank
N.L.O. Normal Lubricating Oil Tank

The tanks of a conventional submarine.

Those are the tanks. Now let us see how the submarine skipper uses them in diving and surfacing.

When ready to get under way, the diving officer calculates the weights of the elements of the ship: stores, ammunition, fuel, and equipment. He also takes into account the distribution of those weights to determine their effect upon trim as well as buoyancy. He then floods the negative tank, the safety tank, and the water round torpedo tanks. Finally he floods the trim tanks and the auxiliary tanks as much as is necessary to put the ship in a condition in which flooding the main ballast and bow buoyancy tanks will bring about negative buoyancy. With all tanks flooded, except main ballast and bow buoyancy, the ship has been trimmed to compensate for the weight it is carrying. It is riding on an even keel with proper positive buoyancy for surface operation.

To dive, the captain gives the order to flood the main ballast tanks and the bow buoyancy tank. The ship then takes on negative buoyancy, and has a down angle because of the effect of the negative tank which is, you remember, forward of the center.

Negative buoyancy is a very desirable thing for purposes of getting the ship started down. But it is not a condition to be allowed to continue, for the ship is literally sinking. To check the sinking and rig the ship for neutral buoyancy, the captain must next reduce the weight of his vessel. He does this by blowing the negative tank, using high-pressure air (3,000 pounds per square inch) from the ship's flasks.

Our submarine operating submerged is in a state of neutral buoyancy; in other words, its weight is equal to the weight of the water it has displaced by submerging. To become a surface ship once more the weight of the submarine must be reduced to bring about a condition of positive buoyancy. Blowing the water from the main ballast tanks and the bow buoyancy tank does the trick very nicely.

Blowing the main ballast tanks alone would give the submarine more than enough positive buoyancy to rise to the surface. But the bow buoyancy tank is also blown to give the ship an up angle, facilitating its rise to the surface under the power of its motors. It would be ungraceful to have the ship come up stern first.

The main ballast tanks are blown by the use of 600-pound air. The bow buoyancy tank is blown with 3,000-pound air. The higher pressure air is used to blow the bow buoyancy tank because it is desirable to attain the up angle immediately when initiating an ascent. Submariners are miserly in the use of compressed air, for it has to be stored in flasks pumped up while the ship is on the surface. In the exigencies of wartime operation, a submarine might find, upon surfacing, that it had to dive right away with no time to recharge the flasks. Hence, it is a rule aboard undersea craft to use as little compressed air as possible and in blowing the main ballast tanks for example, 600-pound air is used only to drive out enough water to give the ship sufficient positive buoyancy to get to the surface. The tanks are not entirely empty and the remaining water is blown by the use of a low-pressure blower, when the submarine reaches the surface. Thus, the variable ballast tanks are usually not blown when the submarine surfaces. The reason is that so long as those tanks contain the correct weights of water the ship is in diving trim, ready to go below simply by flooding the main ballast and bow buoyancy tanks.

The negative tank, which was blown after the dive started in order to effect neutral buoyancy, is flooded when the ship surfaces to complete the process of putting it back into diving trim.

The design of the tanks we have mentioned is an efficient one but it has evolved slowly from the mistakes made by early experimenters in submersible construction. The need for buoyancy control was early recognized, and the solution seen in the use of tanks which could be flooded or vented. But the design of the tanks was not always well thought out. A submarine built in England by Nordenfeldt and Garrett, a decade before *Holland* was accepted by the United States Navy, illustrated the consequences of poorly designed main ballast tanks.

The Nordenfeldt-Garrett boat had nine ballast tanks. For normal submergence the tanks needed to be only partially filled. On its trials, the ship was angled down for a dive. Water in the partially filled tanks immediately surged forward and the craft took on an alarming downward tilt. Prompt pumping and frantic manipulation of the steering controls checked the dive toward doom, but immediately introduced a sharp up tilt. The boat leaped partly clear of the water as it broached. The Nordenfeldt-Garrett craft was not a success.

To avoid the embarrassment of free water in modern submarine ballast tanks, the tanks themselves are compartmented. Whenever flooding is undertaken, groups of main ballast tanks are completely filled and free-water effect is thus eliminated in those tanks.

Free oil in a submarine's fuel tanks could be as disturbing as free water in the ballast tanks. Hence, the tanks must be kept filled as the oil is drawn out for the Diesel engines. This is accomplished by replacing fuel oil with sea water, a feasible operation because the difference in density between oil and water keeps the latter at the bottom of the tank, leaving the fuel oil substantially uncontaminated.

Even now, a submariner's problems are not over. The firing of a torpedo, for example, creates a sudden weight-shift condition. A torpedo weighs nearly 2 tons and its sudden departure from a firing tube causes a radical change in weight precisely where it has the maximum effect upon the trim of the submarine—the bow or stern. Uncorrected, it would cause the submarine's end to rise sharply with resulting exposure to the enemy.

The torpedo is usually fired from the tube by high-pressure air. That air would bar the immediate entry of sea water were it not for the fact that submarine tubes are fitted with poppet valves which release the high-pressure air from the tube as soon as the torpedo is on its way. Sea water rushes in and trim is restored.

By this time you have probably begun to appreciate the large part tanks play in the care and control of a modern submarine. Actually, those mentioned so far are only a few of the variety built into an undersea boat. You name it, the submariner has a tank for it.

There are normal fuel oil tanks, fuel ballast tanks, clean fuel oil tanks (which carry the fuel oil that has been filtered from the fuel ballast tanks and normal fuel tanks), a collecting and expansion tank, lubricating oil tanks, fresh water tanks, battery water tanks, sanitary tanks for the heads (toilets, to landlubbers), hydraulic system supply and vent tanks, a vapor desuperheater tank, torpedo alcohol tanks, torpedo oil tanks, and compressor oil tanks.

But those which we discussed in detail are the ones which affect that most important characteristic of the submarine—its buoyancy.

Tanks play a most important role in the diving and surfacing of a submarine. But ascent and descent are not accomplished by tanks alone. The submarine has to be steered. Like an airplane, it must be steered to right and left and also upward and downward.

Steering to right and left is accomplished by a vertical rudder just as in a surface ship. Steering upward and downward is effected by two pairs of horizontal rudders on either side of the hull. These are called *diving planes* and one pair is located near the bow, the other near the stern. When the submarine starts its dive, the bow planes are tilted to force the bow down, and the stern planes are tilted to assist further in giving the ship a down angle. The negative buoyancy of the filled tanks, the down angle imparted by the action of the diving planes, and the thrust of the propellers send the ship into the depths.

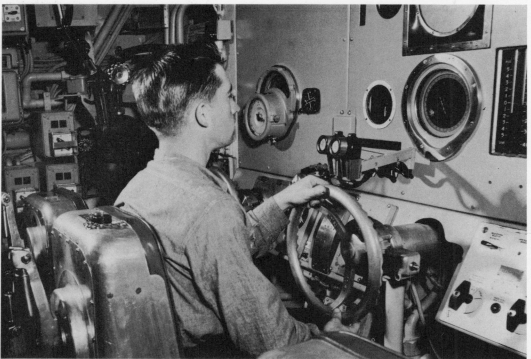

In a conventional submarine, the rudder, forward diving planes, and after diving planes are controlled by three men (top). But so swiftly does U.S.S Nautilus maneuver that a single pilot replaces the three operators (bottom).

In actual fact, the pressure hull and the outer hull which surround it are all that the submarine would need to operate beneath the surface. But conventional submarines of prenuclear design spend most of their time on the surface, and even atom-driven *Nautilus* must come to the surface now and then. Hence, the submarine must add to its two hulls certain accessories essential to surface navigation.

All the upper works built on the top of the hull are called collectively the *superstructure*. This provides a streamlined covering for the numerous protuberances on top of the hull.

The *main deck* of the submarine, extending almost the entire length of the outer hull, is part of the superstructure. Beneath it are ballast tank vents, frames, and outer hull externals of low height. The space between the hull and the main deck is always open to the sea through a series of passages pierced along its sides. This is to avoid the entrapment of air which would affect the submarine's buoyancy and also permits air vented from the tanks to escape to the sea.

The *bridge superstructure* is the high, towerlike part of the superstructure. Called in submarine language the "sail," it is a streamlined enclosure designed to reduce the underwater resistance of a number of submarine fittings which it encloses. Those fittings include the periscopes, radar and radio antennas, snorkel, and main air induction intake.

The sail also encloses the conning tower or, in those submarines which do not have a conning tower, a bridge access trunk which leads from the pressure hull to the navigating bridge high on the superstructure. Both conning towers and bridge access trunks are fitted with watertight hatches at pressure hull level and at their upper end. Under normal circumstances, the upper hatch prevents entry of water into the structure, and in the event of damage to the trunk or conning tower incident to collision, the lower hatch prevents water which enters the conning tower or access hatch from flooding the pressure hull and thus sinking the ship.

The sail structure is open to the sea just as is the main deck. It fills with water when submerged, and drains when the ship surfaces. The conning tower and other fittings which it encloses are, of course, watertight.

At the top of the conning tower or bridge access trunk is the navigating bridge, and when running on the surface, the submarine is conned from that point.

Since the superstructure is a feature of the submarine in its role of surface vessel, it includes a sharp bow to give increased efficiency where the ship cuts the water at the surface. At best, the superstructure makes the submarine only an indifferently effective surface ship. The superstructure is a dead loss to the submerged boat, for its shape is a far cry from the smooth, fishlike contour best for underwater performance. It is significant that the United States Navy's *Albacore*, which has a minimum of superstructure and follows as closely as possible the fish outline, is faster submerged than on the surface.

The submarine designer must pierce his pressure hull on the top with hatches. These entrance ways to the inner hull provide for the loading of stores and ammunition and the entry and exit of personnel. Of major importance is the hatch which permits egress from the escape compartment of a sunken submarine.

To increase the ship's safety, the hull of a submarine is divided into sections at various points along its length. Quick-closing watertight doors can seal off a damaged section to prevent flooding of the entire ship. In the conventional submarine compartmentation, the hull divisions are: forward torpedo room, forward battery compartment, control room, after battery compartment, forward engine room, after engine room, maneuvering room, and after torpedo room.

Drill in emergency closing of watertight doors is an emphasized part of submarine routine. It paid off aboard the American submarine *Squalus* on May 23, 1939.

Squalus, a fleet-type submarine recently commissioned, was making a practice run off Portsmouth, New Hampshire. On board were sixty-two officers and men under command of Lieutenant Oliver Naquin. The order was given to rig for diving. All stations reported ready. *Squalus* started down.

As the conning tower went under, it happened. Water poured into the ship. The main air induction valve, through which air was drawn to supply the Diesel engines when the ship was running on the surface, had failed to close. Seconds were vital. Lieutenant Naquin gave the order to close all watertight access doors.

Despite the speed with which the doors were shut, *Squalus* had taken aboard so much water in the flooded compartments that blowing tanks was not sufficient to regain positive buoyancy. *Squalus* sank to the bottom but was able to release an emergency sea-marker buoy. Rescue ships rushed to the scene. Thirty-three men were brought out alive with the help of a rescue chamber.

The terrible decision to seal off a flooding compartment and thus to doom those shipmates trapped within is one from which there can be no shrinking. If that action is not taken, all hands are marked for death. If doors are promptly closed, some may live.

The sequence of events in diving a submarine requires complex teamwork, for failure at any stage can mean swift tragedy. All hatches are secured in watertight condition. Negative buoyancy is attained by appropriate flooding. Diesel engines are secured and the main air induction valve is closed. Diving planes are tilted. Electric motors turn the propellers. The ship dives beneath the surface.

The consequences of failure in any of these operations are easily appreciated. An open hatch will flood the ship. So will an open air induction valve. If the variable ballast tanks are flooded excessively, too much negative buoyancy may send the ship to dangerous depths. If diving planes jam in diving position, the ship may nose over too sharply and be unable to pull out.

Checking the "Christmas tree." A submarine crew member watches for light signals which will indicate that the ship is in watertight condition for diving.

To help guard against submergence with one or more essential conditions not satisfied, the main control room of a submarine is fitted with a board on which electric lights indicate key situations throughout the boat. Early-type boards displayed red and green lights, and were hence called in submarine slang "Christmas trees." When the board was all green, the ship was safe for diving. Or, anyhow, it should have been. But submariners still remember that the board was all green when *Squalus* went down. Only personal inspection and unrelenting vigilance can verify the indications of the board.

In newly built submarines, the board no longer displays red and green lights. The Navy has accepted the theory that shapes are more significant than colors, and when the ship is ready for diving, the present board shows all horizontal bars. If any situation is not correct for diving, it is revealed by a circular shape on the board. The color for both bars and circles is red.

When the board shows all horizontal lines, the ship is ready for diving and the diving officer reports: "Straight board!"

Despite the number and complexity of operations necessary to get a submarine started downward, a well-trained American crew can completely submerge a fleet-type submarine in less than one minute from the time the command "Dive! Dive!" is given by the captain.

A submarine can dive and climb at very steep angles, but as a rule the ship is not inclined at an angle greater than about 15 degrees. A steeper angle of dive could lift the stern out of water, causing loss of power as a result of elevating the propellers above the surface. In addition, a diving officer must anticipate the action of his ship in order to level off at a predetermined depth. He begins to ease the dive before the desired depth is reached. At a steep angle, that would be a difficult operation.

The maneuvering of a conventional submarine requires that three men handle the steering controls. One man handles the rudder, a second the forward diving planes, and the third the after diving planes. But with the coming of the "true submarine" of the atom-powered age, the old order of maneuvering is changing. Changes of course and angle of climb or dive, rather deliberate business, can now be made as quickly as changes in the heading and climb angle of an airplane. New maneuvering capabilities, for instance, are being developed in *Albacore,* the experimental submarine with the fishlike configuration.

Albacore is not even an atom-powered submarine. When submerged, however, she is driven by a remarkably powerful electric battery and for short distances she is capable of very high—and classified—submerged speeds. On the basis of her performance, innovations in the design of future nuclear-powered submarines will give those vessels capabilities that would have sounded fantastic in the era before the atomic propulsion plant.

So swiftly does *Albacore* maneuver that the old system of three men handling controls under the direction of the diving officer would not work. Their coordination would not be sufficiently rapid or close. In *Albacore,* the three controlmen have been replaced by one man called the pilot. Safety-belted in his seat, he controls the ship's movements by a yoke similar to that used by the pilot of a transport aircraft. Forward and backward motion of the yoke sends *Albacore* diving or climbing. Rotation of the wheel on the yoke turns *Albacore* to right or left.

Instruments showing depth, rate of climb (or dive), speed, heading, and fore-and-aft angle of inclination are mounted on a board in front of the *Albacore* pilot. He controls the submarine much the same as an aircraft pilot flies on instruments. In fact, naval aviators adapt readily to piloting *Albacore.*

Like her air-borne contemporaries, *Albacore* also has an automatic pilot which will maintain her on a constant heading at a constant depth. In addition, it will take her to a new heading and depth once the data are cranked in by the pilot.

The competition between the submarine and the antisubmarine forces has always been keen. Hampered by slow submerged speed, limited maneuverability, and short underwater endurance, the old-style submarine still managed to be a target so difficult that it survived to sink more ships than any other instrument of sea warfare.

Given the potential of atomic power, the maneuverability of *Albacore* hull design, and the missile weapons of the present and near-future, the submarine can scarcely avoid becoming the most potent weapon of war yet developed by man.

Speaking of the advances made in the *Albacore* hull design, Rear Admiral A. G. Mumma, Chief of the Bureau of Ships, said:

"When applied to our fleet of nuclear-powered boats, it will turn submarines into almost undetectable weapons against which there is almost no defense."

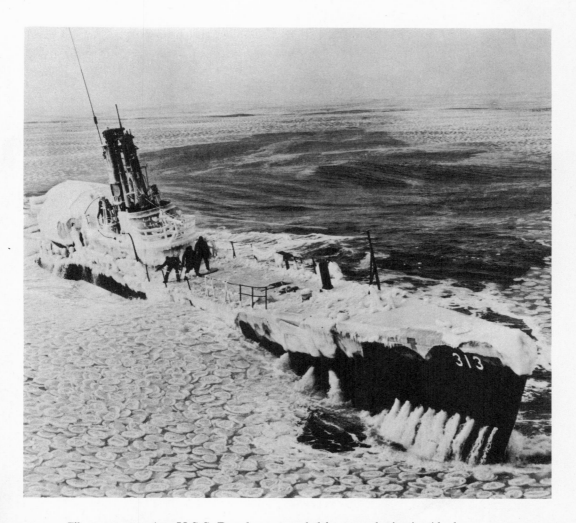

The troop-carrying U.S.S. Perch *surrounded by pancake ice in Alaskan waters demonstrates the all-weather, all-climate capability of the United States submarine.*

5. *Eyes and Ears*

IN MANY WAYS man's conquest of the ocean depths is more remarkable than his struggle to fly through the air. By nature an earth-bound creature, man had to resort to intelligence, science, vision, and hard work to attain the things which to fish came quite naturally. In the air at least, man can see, he can hear, he can breathe, and although a kind Providence saw to it that the human race was essentially waterproof, prolonged submergence capability was not a built-in characteristic.

For all practical purposes, man submerged is dumb, blind, unable to breathe, and with the acuity of all his senses diminished in varying degrees. Bushnell's *Turtle* partially solved only one of these problems; the operator could breathe for a limited time in the pocket of air trapped in *Turtle's* hull. But in order to see, hear, navigate, and approach his target, the one-man captain and crew was required, literally and figuratively, to stick his neck out. This brave act momentarily eliminated the submersible's primary advantage: concealment and surprise.

The answer to the problem of seeing while reasonably well submerged is the periscope. The first periscope used in the United States Navy was an impromptu device employed in a surface ship, the Union monitor *Osage*. During the Civil War, *Osage* ran aground in the Red River and came under heavy Confederate gunfire. Since no one could remain on deck under the withering enemy fire, the captain devised a makeshift periscope from a piece of pipe and two mirrors which enabled him to direct gunfire without exposing his crew to the deadly shore batteries.

But the incident remained without sequel and until 1902 submarines suffered from the tremendous disadvantage of almost complete blindness when running submerged. Simon Lake was keenly aware of the submarine's primary weakness, when he said, "Cruising on the surface with the conning tower exposed would only be a target in wartime. I want to get my seeing eye above surface in something so small that it will not attract attention."

Lake did more than merely state the problem, he set about to build a periscope, but the needs of Lake and his submarine were ahead of the technology and science of his time. He talked with those who knew something about optics, but when they found out what he wanted, they joined the many citizens of his day who believed that Simon Lake's mind was not normal. What he had in mind was to assemble at the end of a tube, lenses and prisms which would direct a view of the surface scene down the tube to an eyepiece, mirror, or a piece of white cloth which would serve as a screen.

Lake, however, was not discouraged and he studied all the available books on optics until he had a fair idea of what he wanted. He then bought "as is" a job lot of lenses which he saw in a store window. It included many sizes and descriptions and with these lenses he experimented in his office in Bridgeport, Connecticut. He constructed an apparatus from various combinations of lenses and prisms, and he would poke the experimental device out of the window to try looking around the corner.

One day he hit upon a lucky combination. He could look down the street and see people walking and wagons rolling down to the harbor. But before he could record the proper arrangement, an office boy, seeing the lenses exposed to the rain, pulled the apparatus in and scrambled the magic combination.

Weeks of unsuccessful attempts to recapture the combination of lenses sent Lake packing off to Johns Hopkins University for assistance from a faculty member who was considered the best man on optics in the United States. After listening to Lake's story, he said, "Sorry to disappoint you. You are trying to do the impossible." When told that Lake had already succeeded in doing "the impossible," the professor worked late that night and on the following day was able to describe the optical principle on which the periscope of today is based.

Luck had been with Lake in developing the periscope, and he had been fortunate in " . . . finding an old German who knew more about the practical end of the business of optics than all the rest of America . . . the only man on this side of the water who could make crown glass without which there would have been no prisms."

Lake's periscope, which he called an omniscope, offered vastly improved means of vision. Some of the better features of the omniscope were: sufficient magnification and clearness of optics for night vision, adaptability for other boats as well as Lake-built submarines, special air circulation to prevent clouding of the lenses due to moisture accumulation, and a tilting head to compensate for changes in the boat's trim.

It took a submarine tragedy to teach a key lesson in ship handling. *A-1,* the first British submarine to be equipped with a periscope, was lost in 1904 as a result of poor periscope conning technique. In looking ahead through a small arc of vision the conning officer failed to scan the remainder of the horizon. In consequence, he did not see the steamer *Berwick Castle* closing on a collision course. The steamer, not noticing the periscope crossing her bow, struck the submarine, sending *A-1* and her entire crew to the bottom. This was the first grim lesson in the dire consequences of failing to sweep the entire horizon when navigating by periscope.

As the optics of the periscope improved, the mechanics of the operation kept step. Longer periscopes led to the use of electric motors to raise and lower them. World War I brought such improvements as mechanical means of quickly raising and lowering the periscope tube, better lenses, double tube construction to withstand high water pressure, and still longer periscopes. Yet, the submarine remained a nearsighted monster with a periscope too short for good vision and practically blind at night.

The World War II periscope, however, was a sophisticated piece of hardware and a masterpiece of optical design. Improvement in the mechanism of raising and lowering the periscope and increasing its maximum length to about 40 feet were two notable advances. The most modern optics went into the lens system to eliminate unwanted light refraction and provide a clearer image. Coated lenses, such as most good cameras now have, helped improve the light transmission in periscope optics.

But even the best system of lenses and prisms leaves something to be desired. All the light which strikes the objective lens does not reach the observer, for much of it is absorbed in the periscope itself. Only about 20 per cent of the original light entering from the top of the periscope finds its way through the eyepiece at the bottom.

Most modern submarines now have two periscopes. One gives greater light transmission, but this requires that it have a thicker portion above water. Hence, it is more readily spotted by an enemy searcher. The second periscope is longer, has a thin above-water part and is thus less readily detected. The first described periscope is generally used for night work because of its better light transmission, and in some instances is fitted with a small radar antenna. Both periscopes have etched horizontal and vertical lines, called telemeter scales, which assist the conning officer to determine range of a target. The periscope is also used to determine the target's bearing.

The periscope is raised by hydraulic power to a position where it may be grasped by the two handles used to train the periscope in azimuth toward the direction of viewing. The left training handle adjusts the prism tilt mechanism

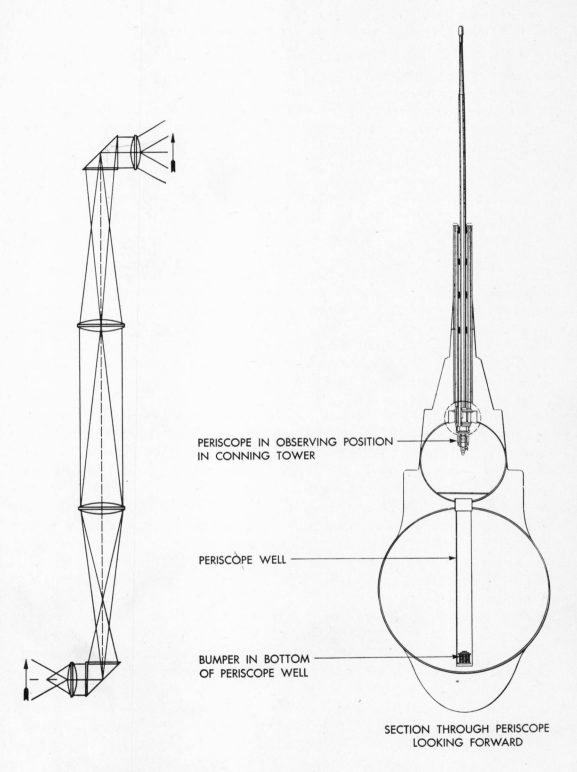

PERISCOPE IN OBSERVING POSITION
IN CONNING TOWER

PERISCOPE WELL

BUMPER IN BOTTOM
OF PERISCOPE WELL

SECTION THROUGH PERISCOPE
LOOKING FORWARD

In the periscope, lenses and prisms bend light rays from the "exit window" at the top through the eyepiece below (left). Submarine cross section shows position of the periscope when extended and the well into which it is retracted (right).

for elevating and depressing the line of sight. The right training handle, when turned, changes the magnification of the image to provide high power or low power.

Magnification of the image is necessary because the image on its way down the periscope goes through a change similar to that which happens when an object is viewed through a pair of field glasses from the wrong end. Everything looks smaller and more distant because the reversed lenses take a wide field of vision and reduce it to a narrow one. Such a miniature view would be unsatisfactory for the submariner because objects could not be easily recognized. To correct this, magnifying lenses in the periscope optical system restore the image to a size large enough for easy perception just before the image is introduced into the eyepiece.

Man under water is by no means deaf and with the assistance of mechanical and electronic aids, the submariner can take advantage of water's ability to transmit sound. Sound waves travel through the water at about 4,800 feet per second, over four times as fast as they travel through the air. Under the right conditions sound which might carry 1 mile through the air can be heard through 10 miles of water. The range of audibility under the water can sometimes extend as far as 50 miles.

It was William Bauer, the German pioneer in submarine construction, who first experimented with submarine signaling a century ago. By striking a piece of submerged metal, he succeeded in signaling across Kronstadt Harbor. This experiment gave rise to a refinement known as the submarine bell which could be lowered from a submarine and sounded by an electric striker. On the receiving end, a submarine skipper could hold the end of a broomstick or a metal bar against his ear with the other end pressed against the hull of the boat, and hear the signals. Fortunately, this was not the last word in communications for the submariner.

Diaphragms mounted on the hull of the submarine provided the next refinement. They picked up submarine signals and transmitted them by flexible tubing to the ear of the listener. During World War I, electrically operated oscillators were perfected, primarily through the efforts of the British Professor Reginald Fessenden. High-frequency alternating current, vibrating a diaphragm, sent short-wave vibrations through the water, and these vibrations permitted a radio operator to send out messages in Morse code.

In addition to providing a channel for underwater communication, however, the property of water to conduct sound waves made possible the development of an underwater detecting device. This device was useful to submarines, but it also became a most important tool for surface ships engaged in anti-submarine warfare. Research in underwater detection during World War I stemmed from the fact that sound waves generated by a vibrating crystal and pitched so high as to be inaudible could be sent out as a beam through the water. Under the sponsorship of the British Anti-Submarine Defense Investi-

Within the crisscross of a periscope's telemeter scales, the camera frames a dramatic moment. Torpedoes from U.S.S. Thresher *destroy an enemy ship, May 1944.*

gation Committee, a detection device was developed which used this super-sonic wave principal. It was called Asdic, a word formed from the Committee's initials.

Asdic is called Sonar (a contraction of *SO*und *NA*vigation and *R*anging) by Americans, and we shall henceforth thus refer to it. It is essentially a system which sends a sharp pulse of supersonic waves through the water. On striking an object such as the hull of a ship, the waves are reflected back toward the sender. The returning echo is picked up by a hydrophone, and the incoming signal is amplified electronically. Since sound waves travel at a known rate of speed through the water, the distance to the object can be calculated on the basis of the time required for the two-way journey of the supersonic waves.

The Germans tried to spoof sonar by the use of a device called *pillenwerfer,* which when released from a submarine generated a cloud of tiny gas bubbles in the water. Sound waves bounce off a cloud of bubbles in much the same way as they do off the hull of a submarine, but expert sonar operators soon learned to detect this deception. Another attempt to foil sonar detection was developed by German scientists and copied by the Japanese. This involved the coating of the submarine's hull and superstructure with a soft rubber com-pound intended to absorb the transmitted sonar signal so that it would not bounce back. It was not effective.

Sonar has an active and a passive application. Active sonar involves the

The eyes and ears of the undersea fleet are both human and electronic. Here they search near and far from the deck of U.S.S. Burrfish, *a radar picket submarine.*

sending of a sound from the submarine in order to detect the existence or range of another object in the water. Passive sonar, however, simply involves listening for sounds generated by another ship or submarine. Such sounds might include propeller noise, engine vibrations, or active sonar in operation from another vessel.

The speed of sound through water is also used as a distance measuring phenomenon, in the fathometer, which bounces sound waves off the ocean bottom and measures the time of their travel. The time interval between impulse and echo gives an accurate indication of the depth and this helps the submarine navigator, who obviously cannot "heave the lead" while submerged.

The submarine's communications facilities include radio, the usual visual devices employed by surface ships, the underwater sound telephone, and active sonar for sending messages by code. The submarine can transmit by radio, however, only when on the surface or sufficiently close to the surface to raise its "periscope antenna." It can receive high radio frequencies only under the same circumstances, but can receive in the VLF (very low frequency) range when completely submerged.

Underwater telephone can be used for short ranges up to 5 miles. This equipment transmits the sound by means of a vibrating diaphragm called a "transducer." The sound carries to the receiving ship where it is picked up by a hydrophone.

World War II brought new eyes which penetrated the blackness of night and made the submarine a scourge of the seas more deadly than ever. These eyes were called radar.

U.S.S. *Plunger* was the first United States submarine to carry radar into war action, but the radar with which *Plunger* was equipped in December 1941 was designed for air search and not for detecting surface ships. It was limited to giving the distance of a plane, but not its direction, and was, therefore, just an electronic alarm to warn a submarine skipper of nearby aircraft.

But by the summer of 1942, surface-search radar equipment was ready for installation on some of the submarines. This radar gave both the bearing and range of a target ship, and as the radar operators became more experienced they could also give a good estimate of a target's size.

Submariners soon learned, however, that detection was a two-way street. If a submarine surfaced to look, she could be seen. If she sent a ping through the water for a range and bearing, she herself might be detected by sonar. Radar likewise could inform as well as detect an enemy, for with an antenna capable of receiving the submarine's radar emission, an enemy might track the submarine without even using his own radar.

Despite this two-way road of mutual detection, however, the submarine still has the option of disappearing from sight when it chooses. The submarine can disappear from both the eyes of man and radar simply by submerging, a unique advantage not shared by the airplane or the surface vessel. Once submerged the submarine remains an evasive shadow, an elusive sound contact in the deep waters which cover most of the earth.

Equipped to hunt and destroy enemy submarines, the U.S.S. Barracuda *carries specialized sound detection apparatus in the large dome at her bow.*

6. *Submarine Weapons*

CREDIT FOR INVENTION of the first effective submarine weapon must be given to David Bushnell, the Connecticut Yankee. Starting with a few ounces of powder and working up to many pounds, he conducted a series of experiments which demonstrated the immense force of underwater explosions, and then used the knowledge to design the armament of *Turtle,* the first submarine to attempt to sink an enemy man-of-war.

Bushnell's powder magazine had severe limitations: The target had to be at anchor and had to have a wooden hull. Otherwise, the operator of *Turtle* could not rest against the bottom of the target and affix the wood screw which held the magazine in place. As we have already seen, *Turtle's* one try with this weapon, in 1776, was foiled by the target's bottom, for Sergeant Ezra Lee, the operator, could not get the screw into H.M.S. *Eagle's* copper sheathing.

Improvements in Bushnell's simple device evolved slowly. Robert Fulton, for example, replaced Bushnell's clockwork firing mechanism with a pistol-and-lanyard firing device which permitted the intrepid submariner to get away from the target before the explosive charge was set off. In 1805, during his experiments in England, Fulton's device blasted the bottom out of the brig *Dorothea,* to the great delight of William Pitt and the consternation of Earl St. Vincent, First Lord of the Admiralty. Though the British sea lords would have nothing to do with Fulton's devilish contrivance, they did pin a label on it which has stuck to this day. They called the underwater explosive charge a "torpedo," which is a kind of ray fish that stuns its victims by discharging a powerful electric shock.

In 1855, William Bauer introduced a novel and dubious weapon. He fixed a magazine or "torpedo" containing 500 pounds of explosive on the bow of the submersible *Marine Devil,* which he built for the Russians. A pair of long rubber gloves was also fitted in the bow of the craft. The object was for the submarine to sneak up to an enemy ship, so that the operator could slip his arms and hands into the rubber gloves from inside the submarine, detach the torpedo from *Marine Devil,* and attach it to the target. There is no record that this was ever really accomplished.

The first submarine weapon to sink an enemy ship was the spar torpedo fitted to the C.S.S. *Hunley.* The Confederate submarine's torpedo consisted of 100 pounds of gunpowder, designed to explode on contact, fixed to the end of a boom about 20 feet long. When not attacking, the spar was held up in the air to prevent the torpedo from striking a floating object and exploding prematurely. Just before the attack it was lowered into position. The advantages of *Hunley's* weapon over those tried before was that it enabled the submarine to strike a moving target. But the spar torpedo still required that the submarine come to dangerously close quarters with its intended victim.

In 1864, at about the same time as *Hunley's* historic attack, Captain Gio-

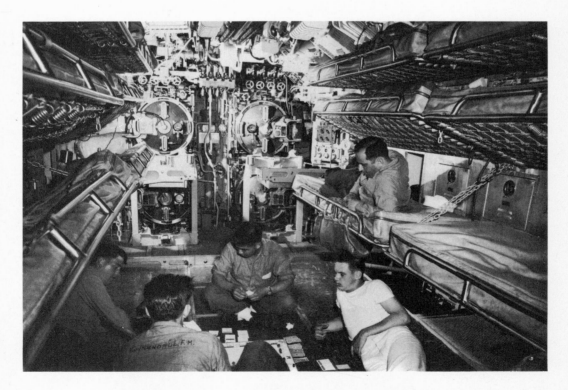

Off-duty relaxation in the torpedo room of the U.S.S. Tang.

vanni Luppis, of the Austrian Navy, presented a plan to his government for building a torpedo which would run under its own power. The idea was to run the torpedo on the surface and guide it by ropes. The nose of the torpedo was to be filled with gunpowder, which would be set off by a pistol, or exploder, on contact with the target. Government authorities told him that his plan was impracticable because there was no engine capable of running such a device independently. So Luppis took his problem to Robert Whitehead. Whitehead liked the idea, but thought it would be better to run the torpedo underwater and to make it self-steering. His engineering mind could not accept the cumbersome guiding ropes.

After two years of hard work, in which he was assisted only by his twelve-year-old son and one workman, Whitehead succeeded in building the first "automobile torpedo." That first model was 14 inches in diameter and was designed to carry 18 pounds of dynamite. Driven by a 3-cylinder reciprocating engine using air compressed to 700 pounds per square inch, it could make a speed of 6 knots for 200 yards. But even for that short distance, Whitehead's first torpedo would not hold its depth. Sometimes it would run on the surface; sometimes it would dive to the bottom.

By 1868, Whitehead had perfected a device called a "balance chamber" which kept his torpedo from acting like a frightened porpoise. For twenty-five years thereafter, the balance chamber was referred to as "The Secret," but we now know that the device consisted of a hydrostatic piston and a pendulum working together to control the horizontal rudders. Water pressure acted on one side of the piston and a steel spring on the other. Thus the piston could be set for the depth desired, while the pendulum acted to keep the torpedo from pitching up and down during its run. Basically the same mechanism is used on torpedoes today.

Torpedoes fitted with "The Secret" ran so well that in 1870 a committee of British officers on duty in the Mediterranean prevailed on the British government to invite Whitehead to come home to England. He accepted the invitation, and took with him two torpedoes. One was the same size as his first model; the other was larger, being 16 inches in diameter and designed to carry an explosive charge of 67 pounds of guncotton. The larger model could make a speed of 7 to 8 knots for a distance of 600 yards.

A committee of naval officers was assigned to investigate Whitehead's torpedoes. After they witnessed over a hundred test runs, the members of the committee reported the following unanimous opinion:

"Any maritime nation failing to provide itself with submarine locomotive torpedoes would be neglecting a great source of power both for offence and defence."

Proponents of the broadside-cannon brand of ordnance scoffed, but over their protests, the British government paid £15,000 for Whitehead's designs and the right to manufacture torpedoes in England. Whitehead developed his torpedo for use by surface craft, called torpedo boats. But his missile found its most effective employment in dramatic union with its natural partner—the submarine.

France, Italy, and Germany were quick to follow England's lead in building torpedoes. Germany established a factory to produce Schwartzkopff torpedoes, based on the Whitehead design. Torpedoes not needed for German use were sold to Russia, Japan, and Spain.

In America, Commander John A. Howell, U.S.N., developed a torpedo driven by energy stored in a large flywheel. For one minute prior to launching, the flywheel was spun by a steam turbine to get it up to speed. In its first successful trial in 1884, Howell's torpedo made 15 knots for over 200 yards. A unique feature of the torpedo was that the same flywheel was used to keep it running on a straight course. Thus, Commander Howell was the first to use a gyroscope to direct a torpedo.

In 1895, Ludwig Obry, a retired Austrian naval engineer, perfected a gyroscopic system for steering the Whitehead torpedo. His system consisted of a small gyroscope mounted on gimbals in the vertical position. A hand-wound spring, triggered on firing, spun the gyro at over 2,000 r.p.m. within a fraction of a second. When the torpedo turned from its intended course, the gyro, remaining fixed in its original direction, sent an error signal to a steering engine which moved the vertical rudders in the proper direction.

The United States Navy decided in favor of the Whitehead torpedo over the Howell in 1897, and, in 1901, the E. W. Bliss Company of Brooklyn, New York, bought the right to manufacture torpedoes under the Whitehead patents. Bliss substituted a turbine for the Whitehead reciprocating engine and used heated high-pressure air to run the turbine. That design was incorporated in the first American-made submarine torpedo, which achieved a speed of 28 knots for 2,000 yards.

In 1908, the Navy established a torpedo factory at the Torpedo Station, Newport, Rhode Island, and a few years later Torpedo Station engineers designed the first torpedo to burn alcohol with compressed air in a com-

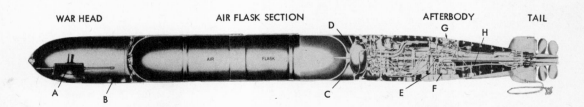

Cutaway view of a steam torpedo. A, Exploder mechanism. B, Ballast. C, Water compartment. D, Fuel flask. E, Depth mechanism. F, Gyro mechanism. G, Starting gear. H, Connector cable receptacle. The cable transmits setting signals to the gyro and depth mechanisms before the torpedo is fired.

bustion pot. Hot gases of combustion, mixed with water which flashed into steam, were used to run the turbine. This principle was incorporated in the Mark 7 torpedo which made a speed of 32 knots to a maximum range of 4,000 yards, and was the primary weapon of United States submarines in World War I. Not until the last years of World War II did a torpedo based on a different propulsion system come into use in American submarines.

The S-boats, built during the 1920's and part of the fleet in World War II, were armed with Mark 10 torpedoes, with a speed of 36 knots to a maximum range of 3,500 yards. The war head carried 497 pounds of TNT—later changed to 485 pounds of torpex, an even more powerful explosive.

The fleet-type submarines of World War II carried Mark 14 torpedoes, which could be set for a speed of 46 knots for 4,500 yards or, alternately, 32 knots for 9,000 yards. The war head originally contained 507 pounds of TNT. During the war this was boosted to 668 pounds of the more powerful torpex. Experiments showed that when that much torpex exploded against a sheet of air-backed steel ¾-inch thick, the resulting hole measured over 40 feet across—large enough to let in plenty of ocean fast.

Although as we have seen, Germany neglected to start an adequate submarine-building program prior to the beginning of World War II, German engineers had been busy perfecting new types of undersea weapons. Features which had been developed during World War I, but had arrived too late for service, were readied for the new conflict. The World War I standard U-boat torpedo had been a steam-propelled Schwartzkopff, reliable, fairly fast, and of long range. But it had one serious drawback—the exhaust gases caused a visible wake. That simplified the work of vengeful destroyers counterattacking the submarine. To eliminate that trouble, German ordnance engineers produced an electric-propelled torpedo. In addition to electric propulsion, the engineers made what appeared to be an even greater contribution in the design of exploders. Previous torpedoes had to hit the target to cause an explosion of the war head. The Germans now designed an exploder which was sensitive to the magnetic field that surrounds any iron or steel body, such as the hull of a ship. The magnetic-influence exploder consisted of a wound armature connected to an electric switch. A change in magnetic field would produce a current in the armature causing the switch to close; the switch then passed electric current from a dry-cell battery to a fine wire in the war-head detonator, which became red hot, causing the detonator to explode the war head. In addition, the new exploder was so designed that it would detonate on contact with a target.

Fascinated with these triumphs, technicians paid little heed to what had heretofore been an important characteristic of torpedoes—their ability to maintain accurately a set depth. Since explosion resulted from magnetic influence, they pointed out, what did it matter that the torpedo might run a few feet off its set depth? Unfortunately for U-boat captains, the engineers

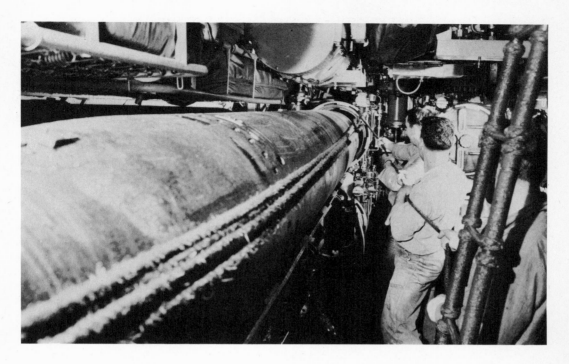

In loading a torpedo, a tackle is used to move it from its skid into the tube.

had failed to test their new designs thoroughly. The magnetic exploder turned out to be a lemon. Sometimes it failed to work at all; other times it caused the torpedo to explode prematurely, warning the intended victim of the presence of a U-boat and bringing swift counterattack from escort ships.

On September 14, 1939, for example, *U-39* fired a torpedo with a magnetic exploder at the British aircraft carrier *Ark Royal*. Its premature explosion brought about the loss of the submarine. In early 1940, German torpedoes running too deep spared the battleship *Warspite* at Narvik and British transports at Harstad. Tests showed that part of the trouble lay in the malfunctioning of the magnetic exploder. But a contributing factor was that the torpedoes in some instances ran so deep—due to faulty depth-control mechanisms—that the magnetic field of the target was too weak to actuate the exploder.

Wartime submarining is a dangerous business. Those who volunteer to serve do so with open eyes. But to undergo the hazards only to find oneself powerless because of defective weapons can wreck the morale of the bravest. As the morale of the U-boat force reached its lowest point, Admiral Doenitz took personal charge of the situation. Erratic electric torpedoes and temperamental magnetic exploders were withdrawn from service. Steam-driven torpedoes with the old reliable contact exploders were issued to the U-boats, and Doenitz demanded an immediate corrective program on the electric torpedo and the magnetic exploder.

The new weapons were redesigned. Good depth-keeping control was combined with the wakeless electric drive. Reliability was built into the magnetic ploder. The torpedoes thus improved were returned to action in the summer of 1941 and gave satisfactory service.

The United States entered the war two years after Great Britain declared war on Germany. We did not, unfortunately, have the benefit of full reports on German torpedo troubles. Our own were tragically parallel.

In the first weeks of the war for instance, the fleet-submarine *Sargo,* commanded by Lieutenant Commander T. D. Jacobs, made eight attacks on Japanese ships in the South China Sea. All attacks were in daylight with good visibility. Thirteen Mark 14 torpedoes were fired. None exploded.

As evidence of faulty torpedoes mounted, Rear Admiral Charles A. Lockwood, Commander Submarines Southwest Pacific, started an investigation of the Mark 14. In June and July 1942, shots through a fishnet placed approximately 900 yards from firing submarines indicated that the Mark 14's were running at least 10 feet deeper than set. On August 1, 1942, the Bureau of Ordnance stated that tests conducted at Newport substantially confirmed the Pacific tests. The pioneer skippers were vindicated.

Although submariners started to set their torpedoes shallower to allow for the depth error, their troubles were not over. On April 9, 1943, for example, *Tunny,* Lieutenant Commander J. A. Scott commanding, fired ten Mark 14 torpedoes at two Japanese aircraft carriers. Seven explosions were heard. Seven hits should have blasted as many 40-foot holes in the bottoms of the targets. The only result was one carrier slightly damaged—because the explosions were premature.

Indications increased that the shallower depth settings caused the torpedoes to explode prematurely more often. In June 1943, Admiral Lockwood, now Commander Submarines Pacific Fleet, ordered inactivation of the magnetic feature of the exploder, retaining only contact components. The following March, Southwest Pacific submarines followed suit.

But still one more flaw in their primary weapon plagued the submariners. On August 6, 1943, Lieutenant Commander L. R. Daspit brought *Tinosa* into Pearl Harbor and reported that his submarine had fired eleven torpedoes which hit the 19,000-ton *Tonan Maru* squarely but which failed to explode. The torpedoes were Mark 14's with the magnetic feature of the exploder inactivated.

An immediate answer to this dud problem was mandatory. Captain C. B. Momsen, Commander Submarine Squadron Two, recommended that a number of torpedoes be tested by firing them against the cliffs on the island of Kahoolawe. Three torpedoes, complete with live war heads and exploders, were fired. The first two exploded; the third was a dud. With the aid of several officers and men who were accomplished skin divers, the faulty torpedo was brought up from the bottom. When the exploder—cradled inside over 600 pounds of high explosive—was removed with great care, examination showed that the torpedo had struck the cliff squarely, mashing the nose of the war head and damaging the exploder mechanism—before the firing pin could set off the explosion!

Further tests, dropping dummy war heads from a height of 90 feet, showed that torpedoes which hit *squarely* damaged the exploder more than those which hit *obliquely*. Within three weeks, modifications to the firing pin remedied the contact-exploder troubles. Finally, by late 1943, United States submarines were armed with fairly reliable torpedoes.

Then in September 1943, a new submarine torpedo was pressed into service in the Pacific: the Mark 18, copied from the German electric-driven model. Manufactured by the Westinghouse Electric Corporation, it was wakeless and had excellent depth performance, though still inferior to the Mark 14 in speed and range. In spite of its top speed of 29 knots, as compared with the 46 knots of the Mark 14, the Mark 18 torpedo became the favorite of most submariners in the last year of the war. Unlike the steam-driven Mark 14, it left no visible wake.

While United States ordnance designers were copying the electric torpedo, German U-boats returned to the Battle of the Atlantic armed with a torpedo designed on an entirely new principle. Instead of intercepting the target on a straight course, the new torpedo listened for the noise of the target's propellers. When it heard propeller noise, its sonic homing system took charge of the torpedo rudders and steered to the source of the noise. After losing several escort ships to this weapon, the British learned to slow their propellers when a U-boat was detected within homing-torpedo range. The Germans countered by increasing the sensitivity of the acoustic homing circuit so that the torpedo would home on the noise of ship's pumps, generators, and ventilating fans. After that the British started streaming noisemakers, called "foxers," astern of their escorts to decoy the homing torpedo away from its target. The acoustic torpedo attacks on the foxer were harmless.

In the last year of the war in the Pacific, United States submarines used acoustic homing torpedoes of American design. Several Japanese patrol craft and frigate types were sunk by the homing weapons. The Japanese Navy was much too hard pressed by that time to produce a countermeasure to a new secret weapon.

The submarine torpedo is an active weapon, since it is capable of self-propulsion to reach its target. The submarine mine, on the other hand, is a passive weapon—deposited in a strategic location, it lies in wait for unsuspecting ships to pass close enough to cause their own destruction.

Submarines make good offensive mine-layers because they can do the job accurately and with maximum secrecy. The first submarines to conduct an effective mining campaign were the German C-class boats of World War I. Operating from Zeebrugge they infested the approaches to the Thames with numerous fields of their deadly eggs. On September 20, 1915, the German Supreme Command ordered U-boats to cease all commerce raiding around the British Isles. After that, mine-laying attained major importance—it was not considered commerce raiding.

At that time, necessity again mothered invention. The Germans developed mines that could be fired from U-boat torpedo tubes, which simple expedient made mine-layers out of all U-boats. The German Navy continued mine-laying throughout the war, and by 1917 the British were forced to employ over 3,000 mine-sweeping craft to counter the U-boat mining campaign.

The British built five mine-laying submarines as part of the War Emergency Programme ordered by Winston Churchill in 1914. In March 1916, one of these, *E-24,* became the first British submarine to plant an offensive mine field when she bottled up the U-boat exit at the mouth of the Elbe. After the war, the British converted an incomplete hull to an experimental mine-laying submarine. Designated *M-3,* she carried mines on rails located on top of the hull. They could be laid, either surfaced or submerged, by being moved along the rails until they dropped over the stern. *M-3* was a complete success, but no more were built.

The start of World War II found the German U-boats better armed with their new mines than with their troublesome torpedoes. Their magnetic mines were excellent and reliable, and U-boats sowed them in great numbers in British harbor approaches and narrow shipping lanes. The magnetic field surrounding a ship's hull would cause them to explode when the ship passed over —a feature that caught the Allies by surprise, and accounted for many ships before effective countermeasures were produced. To counter these mines many ships were "degaussed"—their magnetic field was reduced by setting up a counterfield in electric cables installed around the hull. The British also developed magnetic sweeps to explode the mines harmlessly.

The first submarine mine field of the Pacific War was planted by the American submarine *Thresher* on October 16, 1942. Lieutenant Commander W. J. Millican, *Thresher's* captain, took her into the northern part of the Gulf of Siam, where she lay on the bottom the entire day before the mine plant. Surfacing after nightfall, she crept silently and slowly on battery power, firing Mark 12 magnetic mines from her torpedo tubes.

Suddenly one of the mines exploded, sending up a geyser as high as Old Faithful. A minute later another went off just astern of *Thresher.* Millican calmly finished planting all of the mines. Later he reported to headquarters, "It must have been caused by personal magnetism."

The great danger of submarine mine-laying is that the submarine must go into shallow, confining waters. To surmount this difficulty the United States Navy has developed mobile mines that run through the water like torpedoes. They can be aimed and preset to run any distance up to several miles. At the end of their run they automatically stop and plant themselves. Using these, submarines can remain in deep water while planting a mine field inside a harbor some distance away.

Submarines have been consistently successful in the use of mines and tor-pedoes, but another submarine weapon, the deck gun, has had its ups and downs. The United States Navy's first submarine, *Holland,* had a fixed gun which could throw 100 pounds of explosive half a mile. It was not a useful weapon, however, and immediate successors to *Holland* dispensed with it.

It was the prize rules of international law, however, which returned the deck gun to prominence early in World War I. The submarine needed a weapon to intimidate merchantmen into stopping for search. Anticipating this need, Germany ordered two types—a 1.45-inch gun on a fixed pedestal mount, and a 12-pounder mounted on a disappearing carriage. By 1916, armed merchantmen and Q-ships had made it too risky for U-boats to follow the stop-and-search procedure, so deck guns became a relatively useless adornment on U-boats.

The British armed their larger World War I submarines with 3-inch rapid-fire guns on disappearing mounts. In February 1916, *E-7* conducted a 24-day foray in the Sea of Marmara, where she outfought a two-gun Turkish gun-boat, and sank twenty-three other Turkish craft. She also destroyed two troop trains, in which engagement she became the first submarine to fight a gun duel with a shore battery.

After the war the British continued to lead the way in development of gun armament for submarines. Their *M-1,* a "monitor" submarine, mounted a 12-inch gun, the largest ever installed on any sub. *M-1* could approach a target submerged with the gun loaded, come up until the muzzle of the gun was out of water, and get off a shot in less than thirty seconds. Unfortunately, *M-1* was rammed by a merchantman and sank. No others like her were built, but British postwar experiments included another unique type. That was *X-1,* a cruiser submarine mounting four 5.2-inch guns in double turrets fore and aft. Completed in 1925, she was the largest submarine ever built by the Royal Navy, 363 feet long and displacing over 3,000 tons.

H.M.S. X-1 *mounted four 5.2-inch guns in double turrets fore and aft.*

The giant French cruiser submarine Surcouf *in drydock, showing the twin 8-inch guns in the streamlined watertight mount forward of the conning tower.*

France followed by launching a cruiser submarine, *Surcouf,* in 1929. She mounted twin 8-inch guns in a streamlined turret forward of the conning tower. In addition, she carried one seaplane in a hangar aft and had ten 21-inch torpedo tubes—a powerful armament in a package 361 feet long and 2,880 tons in displacement. Early in World War II *Surcouf* captured a German merchantman 1,000 miles at sea but later in the war she came to a tragic end. While serving on convoy duty in the North Atlantic, she sank as the consequence of a collision with one of the ships she was escorting.

1943 witnessed the return of the submarine deck gun for a new purpose—antiaircraft defense. Radar-equipped aircraft had driven the U-boats from the surface of the North Atlantic, so, while developing the snorkel, Doenitz armed his conventional submarines with one 37 mm. AA gun, four 20 mm. AA guns, and smaller caliber machine guns. He ordered them, contrary to their usual tactics, to remain on the surface and fight it out with enemy aircraft.

One R.A.F. Beaufighter would customarily force a U-boat down. The first to try it on the newly armed boats were greatly surprised, but after Coastal Command planes suffered some losses, they changed their tactics. Instead of attacking alone, the aircraft would now call in reinforcements, for the conventional U-boat was no match for a force of well-armed aircraft. The Germans doubled the antiaircraft battery of a few undersea craft, which they labeled "flak traps," but instead of falling into the trap, British planes kept out of range of the U-boat guns and demolished the enemy with cannon shells and rocket projectiles. After that, the U-boats returned to their element, underwater where radar and cannon shells cannot penetrate.

The gun crew of U.S.S. Sea Dog *prepare the specially designed 5-inch, 25-caliber submarine gun for action. The first loader holds a shell, ready to ram it home.*

On America's entry into World War II, United States submarines were armed with either a 3-inch or 4-inch deck gun and a smaller caliber machine gun. These were considered too small, however, and a few fleet-type submarines were equipped with a 5-inch, 51-caliber "Long Tom"—originally designed for battleship broadside batteries. In 1944, the Navy completed development of a 5-inch, 25-caliber mount designed specifically for submarines. It was a wet mount type, built of noncorrosive materials that functioned smoothly after long immersion in salt water.

United States submarines used deck guns mainly to sink Japanese sampans and small craft, many of which were used on picket duty around the Japanese islands. They also sank by gunfire nineteen large ships totaling 86,000 tons.

At the end of World War II, a few submariners foresaw that the combination of the submarine and the guided missile would make a potent weapon system in the event of another major conflict. The most satisfactory missile available at the time was the German V-1 "buzz bomb." An American adaptation of V-1, named Loon, was made for shipboard launching. Powered by a single pulsejet engine, Loon reached a top speed of 400 miles per hour at an altitude of 12,000 feet with a maximum flight range of 135 miles.

Two fleet-type submarines, *Carbonero* and *Cusk,* were modified to launch and guide Loon. They launched the missile by firing four rocket boosters, each with a thrust of 11,000 pounds, which were attached to a sled carrying the Loon. The sled and rockets automatically dropped off when the booster motors burned out. The submarine guided Loon by sending radio command signals—right turn, left turn, or dive.

Regulus I missiles stowed in a hangar with upper missile upside down. After the lower missile is launched, the upper missile is turned into the lower position.

On November 7, 1949, *Carbonero* launched a Loon as part of a fleet operation near the Hawaiian Islands. The missile sped over a line of thirty-five surface ships stretched out from 20 to 45 miles from the launching submarine. Antiaircraft guns banged away at the Loon; fighter planes tried to intercept. Loon flew on 40 miles past the ships before the dive command ended the flight. The submarine-launched missile had arrived to stay.

In 1950, Chance Vought Aircraft, Incorporated, of Dallas, Texas, successfully flight-tested a new missile designed for submarine use. That was Regulus, a swept-wing, turbojet-powered craft that could deliver an atomic war head over a range of several hundred miles. Flying at an altitude near the stratosphere, Regulus cruised at a speed of 600 miles per hour.

On March 6, 1953, the United States Navy launched *Tunny*, a fleet-type submarine converted to carry two Regulus missiles. The missiles are stowed in a hangar located on top of the hull just abaft the conning tower, and an access hatch into the hangar permits men to enter and prepare the missile for launching, while the submarine is still submerged.

When a Regulus is ready for launching, *Tunny* surfaces. The hangar door is opened and the missile is rammed out onto a launcher rail on deck. The launcher is elevated to 30 degrees, and the hangar door is shut. Operation of the hangar door and the launcher is by hydraulic rams. The turbojet engine is started and brought up to speed. Then two rocket boosters are ignited, thrusting the missile off the launching rail and up to flight speed. The submarine can then submerge. A complete operation—surfacing, firing a missile, and submerging—can be carried out in a few minutes.

In 1955, another submarine, *Barbero,* was converted to a missile-firing ship like *Tunny.* And a year later construction began on three new guided-missile submarines, one of which was nuclear-powered.

In 1958 the United States Navy was conducting flight tests of Regulus II, a supersonic successor to the original Regulus. At the same time, the development of an intermediate-range ballistic missile for submarine use was making great progress. That missile, Polaris, was designed to use solid rocket fuel. In combination with the nuclear-powered submarine it promised to initiate a new era in mobile, dispersable, intercontinental weapon systems.

In the less than two hundred years that passed since *Turtle's* attempt to attach a few pounds of gunpowder to an anchored ship, submarines developed the capability to deliver the equivalent of millions of tons of TNT to targets anywhere in the world. With the advance of its weapons, the submarine evolved from a hand-powered cockleshell to the nuclear-powered epitome of global firepower.

The Regulus I guided missile is elevated for launching aboard the U.S.S. Tunny *(top), and moments later blasts off trailing a billow of smoke (bottom).*

7. *The Enemy Above*

THE MAIN FUNCTION of warships has always been the sinking of enemy ships. Today, blessed with the hindsight afforded by two world conflicts, we know that the submarine excels at that task. But the submarine's capability was not always recognized.

The introduction of the submarine into naval warfare caught dyed-in-the-wool surface ship strategists totally unprepared to cope with the new dimension in sea warfare. Prior to World War I the superior gun power of surface ships was considered adequate protection against submersibles. Submarines would be caught napping on the surface and destroyed by shells from big guns, the surface men said. Those who did not subscribe to that popular absurdity were called "radical thinkers." But when in September 1914 a single German submarine, *U-9,* sank three British Cressy-class cruisers in a matter of minutes, there was no way of counterattacking the submarine. Naval conservatives were shocked into seeking effective means for sinking submarines.

Desperation bred some rather weird schemes for countering the submarine. One of those ideas was for three picket boats to tow a large net. On sighting the submarine, the two outer boats were supposed to swing the ends of the net around opposite sides, encircling the helpless submersible like some giant fish. Like many desperate measures, this proved to have little chance of success. U-boats refused to co-operate in the process.

In November 1914, when it looked as if there was no defense against the U-boats, the British Navy introduced a clever scheme for baiting the mechanical sharks. Innocent-looking merchantmen were heavily armed and sent to patrol submarine-infested waters around the British Isles. The program was kept highly secret, and the ships were called mystery ships, or Q-ships. After 1915, Q-ships did manage to sink U-boats, but as the effect of surprise wore off, their successes dwindled. U-boat skippers became extremely wary, relying on torpedoes rather than gunfire. Despite their wariness, however, one gallant mystery-ship captain, Commander Gordon Campbell, was still able to outwit the enemy.

On February 17, 1917, Campbell's ship *Farnborough,* renamed *Q-5,* was about 40 miles south of Ireland proceeding eastward at a leisurely 7 knots. A torpedo was sighted headed for the ship. It was far off and could easily have been dodged. But Campbell had given an unprecedented order: "Should the Officer of the Watch see a torpedo coming, he is to increase or decrease speed as necessary to *ensure it hitting"!*

His order was carried out. The torpedo was allowed to blast a gaping hole in the ship's side. As if abandoning ship, panic crews manned the lifeboats and rowed away. But Captain Campbell lay hidden on the bridge, secretly watching the U-boat through a peephole. His fighting crew remained out of sight below decks.

The wary U-boat approached submerged. Its periscope eye peered at every part of *Farnborough,* looking for a sign of life on board. Satisfied there was none, the U-boat captain surfaced his craft 300 yards off *Farnborough's* bow. Campbell had his crew steal topside and hide by their guns. When the submarine—identified as *U-83*—came alongside, *Farnborough* revealed her true identity as *Q-5*—with a 6-pounder shell which struck the U-boat's conning tower and decapitated the captain.

The Q-ship gunners hurled over forty shells at the hapless, surprised U-boat. *U-83* sank. Two of her crew were rescued from the water.

Meanwhile, *Farnborough* was sinking from the torpedo hit which she had accepted. But she had a cargo of timber in her holds, which buoyed her up. She was towed to shore, beached, and repaired to return to service as a cargo carrier.

Captain Campbell was awarded the Victoria Cross for his gallantry. In order to preserve secrecy, the reason for the award was not made public, and Campbell became known as "the Mystery V. C."

In contrast to the glamour and gallantry of World War I, the history of Q-ships in World War II proved to be dismal and disastrous. The British tried them again but gave up in 1941. The United States Navy tried them in 1942 and 1943. The lives of one hundred forty-eight American officers and men were lost, without damage to a single U-boat. Admiral E. J. King stopped this fruitless undertaking.

The Japanese employed a number of Q-ships against United States submarines in the Pacific. Although they were not credited with any confirmed kills, they gave the first submarines to encounter them some uncomfortably close calls.

One Japanese Q-ship was dubbed "Smoky Joe," because of its ruse of letting heavy black smoke pour from its stack. The first submarine to encounter it was *Thresher,* making her third war patrol in 1942. *Thresher* was running submerged off the entrance to Amboina Bay, in the East Indies, while a careful periscope watch was kept on the approaches to the Bay. One periscope sweep revealed a lightly laden merchantman of about 3,000 tons heading out the harbor entrance. It was proceeding at high speed and at intervals black smoke belched from its single funnel.

Lieutenant Commander W. J. Millican maneuvered *Thresher* into attack position—800 yards abeam of the freighter—and fired two torpedoes. Before the torpedoes were halfway to the target, however, a check look with the periscope revealed that the freighter had commenced a 90-degree turn. It was swinging toward the submarine full speed ahead.

Millican had not been quarterback at Annapolis for nothing. The instant the torpedoes were away, he had dodged to get off the tracks. Now he speeded up and went deep.

The Japanese Q-ship churned straight down the center of the torpedo wakes and when it reached the end, it let go a blasting string of fourteen depth charges—right where *Thresher* had been. While "Smoky Joe" continued searching the area and dropping sporadic depth charges, *Thresher* stole away at deep submergence. Millican's subsequent report described the Q-ship and warned other submariners to watch out for it.

But even in World War I, the guns of the Q-ships were not the only antisubmarine weapons. At the outset of the war it had long been known that explosions underwater transmitted terrific pressure waves to considerable distances, and using this principle, the British and French developed an explosive charge for dropping on submarines. The first "depth charges" contained 300 pounds of explosive and would sink at a rate of 6 feet per second. Because of the difficulty involved in actually striking a submerged object with the charge, a mechanism was added which caused it to explode on reaching a set depth. Hydrostatic pressure caused the charge to be set off and if it exploded within about 30 feet of a submarine, water-hammer effect would burst a hole in the submarine's pressure hull. The first United States depth charges had to explode much closer than 30 feet, since they contained only 50 pounds of explosive. In 1919, the United States Navy beefed up their explosive charge to 600 pounds.

With the invention of the depth charge, destroyers came into their own as the primary antisubmarine warship. Those small, fast ships could outrun and outgun a submarine on the surface, and with the addition of depth charges they had a weapon which could sink a submarine even when submerged. The depth charge proved to be the most effective antisubmarine weapon of the war—thirty-five U-boats were sunk by depth-charge attacks.

In 1917, shortly after Germany resorted to unrestricted submarine warfare, the Allies commenced convoy operations. Convoys were not new—for hundreds of years they had been used to protect merchantmen from depradations by enemy men-of-war or pirates. What was new was the protection they now offered to merchant ships from attacks by submarines. By 1918, Britain alone had four hundred destroyers; the Allies boasted a total of nine hundred. Used mainly to escort convoys, theirs is the credit for protecting the troopships which transported Americans to the Continent with very small loss of life.

While the depth charge was the most effective weapon for sinking World War I U-boats, its lethal qualities were limited by lack of good underwater detection equipment. Actually, only one out of five U-boats detected was submerged. The other 80 per cent were seen first on the surface.

Between the two wars, a new device for locating a submerged submarine was developed. This device—called Asdic by the British and Sonar by the Americans—provided accurate range and bearing location on a submerged submarine. But Asdic (or Sonar) had one weakness: it would not keep contact on a target close aboard, particularly if the target were running deep. And U-boats in the second World War were able to operate at much greater depths than their predecessors. An attacking destroyer might maintain good contact with a submarine for some time, only to lose it several hundred feet before a depth-charge attack could be made. The destroyer captain had to estimate where the submarine would be when the charges got there. More often than not, he guessed wrong.

To make the best use of sonar data, it was necessary to develop a missile which could be fired while the attacking ship was still far enough away from the submarine to have good contact. The answer was hedgehog, which could be fired at a range of 250 yards while sonar information was still available. A hedgehog salvo consisted of twenty-four missiles, each containing 31 pounds of high explosive. They were designed to explode on contact, so it was not necessary to know the submarine's depth. They did not go off and roil the water unless a hit was obtained.

Fortunately for United States submarines, the Japanese never adopted hedgehog-type antisubmarine missiles. Their answer to the problem was to use bigger-than-ever depth charges. It was their theory that if the force of the explosion were sufficiently great, accurate placement would not be necessary. They were wrong.

Japanese antisubmarine measures—including surface craft, aircraft, submarines, and mines—took a toll of thirty-eight American submarines in World War II. Another nine were lost due to operational casualties. The reasons for the loss of five more are unknown.

A fully loaded hedgehog consists of twenty-four missiles each containing 31 pounds of high explosive. The hedgehog is designed to sink a submarine on contact.

Hedgehog patterns strike the water as destroyers Sarsfield *and* Epperson *maneuver off the Florida Keys. Hedgehog can be fired effectively at a range of 250 yards.*

U.S.S. Halibut *at Pearl Harbor, survivor of intensive Japanese depth-charging.*

Had the Japanese foreseen the tremendous effect that United States submarines would have on the outcome of the Pacific War, they would have put more emphasis on their antisubmarine fleet in their prewar building period. And even as it was, some of the Japanese antisubmarine fighters were technically capable of playing on anybody's first team.

For example, on November 14, 1944, *Halibut,* skippered by Commander I. J. Galantin, fired four electric torpedoes at a Japanese convoy in Luzon Strait. Six minutes later, there was a buzzing noise followed by a loud explosion like a close depth charge. The buzzing noise was probably from a low-flying aircraft using Magnetic Airborne Detector, a sensitive device that measures the change in the earth's magnetic field due to a mass of steel—such as the hull of a submarine.

The convoy's escort ships picked up the scent and ganged up on *Halibut.* Their first depth-charge attack mashed in the conning tower. The second barrage, overhead, shoved *Halibut* deeper. Inside the submarine, men were thrown into the bilges, torpedoes broke loose, sea valves blew open, air lines burst. Heat and pressure became almost unbearable. But adversity brought out the best in the American submarine crew. The men got up off the deck, made emergency repairs and restored order.

Then the Japanese ships made one mistake—they sped away instead of persisting in their attack. Galantin and his crew were able to bring the ship home, although structural damages proved so severe that *Halibut* had to be retired from active service.

Britain had only one hundred eighty destroyers at the start of World War II—less than half as many as she had in 1918, and not even all of those were equipped with underwater sound-detection equipment. At the same time, the United States Navy had only sixty destroyers fitted with sonar.

While the British Navy was woefully short of antisubmarine craft, the Nazis were even worse off for submarines—they had but fifty-seven, only twenty-two of which could go as far as the Atlantic. When Hitler made mistakes, they were often crucial! That particular mistake presented the Allies with the commodity they needed most—*time!*

But by mid-1941 U-boat numbers were increasing rapidly. Admiral Doenitz had enough to start wolf-pack tactics. He would send a dozen undersea wolves tearing at the throats of lumbering merchant ships herded into convoys like so many sheep. Although British and Canadian escort ships worked day and night in the cold, rough convoy routes, there were too many wolves and not enough sheep dogs.

But in the fall, a new player was added to the defensive team. That was the escort carrier, designed to furnish air cover in the far ocean reaches where wolf packs roamed out of reach of land-based planes. At first both land- and sea-based aircraft acted mainly as a deterrent to daylight surface operation of the U-boats, but they soon took on a more aggressive function.

The U-boats depended on the ability to stay on the surface every twenty-four hours long enough to recharge batteries. That could usually be done under cover of darkness. But in the spring of 1942, surfaced U-boats began to be surprised by aircraft that could see in the dark. The first warning would be the blinding glare of a powerful searchlight from a low-flying plane. The appearance of the light would be followed by a string of bombs. U-boats trying to cross the Bay of Biscay going to and from their lairs on the Atlantic coast of France were attacked around the clock by bombers of the R.A.F. Coastal Command. Many German submariners did not return to tell of their experience. Those who did make it told Doenitz that the British aircraft had a new location device which let them find their target even when the visibility was zero.

There was only one such device known—radar. But that equipment, so far as the Germans knew, was too bulky and heavy to be carried by aircraft. Nevertheless, Doenitz had his radio intelligence branch watch enemy planes for signs that they carried radar. In June 1942, they confirmed his suspicions. Admiral Maertens, Chief of Naval Radio Intelligence, reported that enemy aircraft were using radar for locating targets, and that the wave length of the radar pulses was 1.2 meters.

Using this information, German radar scientists developed receivers that would detect transmissions on the frequencies used by the British. Equipped with those receivers, the U-boats were able to get under before approaching aircraft could make a surprise attack. Thus, in the last six months of 1942 the

Revenge on the seawolves. Specialized radar equipment caught German U-boats on the surface where they were bombed and strafed by land- and sea-based aircraft.

wolf packs made their way from their pens and into the convoy lanes where they destroyed over five hundred Allied ships.

Beginning in 1943, the U-boats began to experience surprise attacks from aircraft once again. Their radar search receivers gave no warning. Finally, in May, the number of U-boats lost in one month reached a total of forty-three, and the ships sunk per U-boat dropped to a small fraction of its former value. Doenitz withdrew the U-boats from the Battle of the Atlantic.

At first the Germans thought that the enemy was detecting radiation from their radar search receivers. That proved to be false. In January 1943, the Germans had salvaged a peculiar apparatus from a British aircraft shot down over Rotterdam. It was not until the following August that they succeeded in getting the damaged equipment reassembled and in working order. When they did, they discovered that the Rotterdam equipment was a radar that transmitted its pulses on the unbelievably (to the Germans) short wave length of only 9 centimeters. Of course, they went right to work to develop a search receiver which would pick up that wave length. The war ended before they succeeded.

Meanwhile, Doenitz attempted to get his U-boats back into the battle by equipping them to fight it out with aircraft, but, as we have seen, they proved no match for teams of rocket-firing Beaufighters. Then the standard types of U-boats were fitted with snorkels, which enabled them to recharge their batteries without surfacing. But the snorkel had to be exposed above the surface to be

A captured German submarine is boarded and taken in tow by the crew of the escort carrier U.S.S. Guadalcanal. *Motor whaleboat from the* Guadalcanal *lends help.*

of any use. Thus, it provided a target for human and electronic eyes, and could not give the submarine the ultimate security from detection that is provided by complete submergence.

It was not until May 1945, that new type U-boats were ready for operations. *U-2511,* the first Type XXI to make a patrol, penetrated a screen of three destroyers and reached position for firing torpedoes against a cruiser—still undetected. But no shots were fired. The war was over.

By dint of tremendous effort, bravery, skill, and persistence, Allied forces defeated the enemy submersibles: seven hundred eighty-two German, eighty-five Italian, and one hundred thirty Japanese submarines were sunk.

But a victory over slow submersibles which had little endurance submerged was in reality a victory over a peculiar type of surface ship. Nautical graybeards may still congratulate themselves over that hard-won victory. The problem is different now.

The most advanced types of German U-boats—Type XXI with its submerged speed of 17 knots and its doubled endurance submerged, and Type

Resting between wars. Decommissioned World War I American destroyers were brought out of mothballs and reconditioned to fight in World War II. Fifty of these ships were exchanged for base rights on British islands in the Western Hemisphere.

XXVI with its hydrogen-peroxide-fed engines giving many days of submerged operation—were signposts of things to come. No longer are submarines constrained by limited mobility to attacks on targets of opportunity. By contrast, the nuclear-powered submarine is a completely new kind of weapon—it can attack where and when it chooses, it can outspeed surface opponents, it can choose its own battleground. The submersible has been defeated; the submarine has not.

Completed too late for action in World War II, U-2513, a German Type XXI U-boat, was designed with twice the underwater endurance of other U-boats, and with a submerged speed of 17 knots.

A destroyer protects the flank of a convoy against submarine attack.

8. The Submarine Strikes

SUBMARINE COMMANDERS go about their business of sinking enemy ships by using carefully planned tactics and procedures. Rigorous training in these fundamentals prepares the submarine captains to take the right action instantaneously in situations where success or failure, and life or death, depend on their decisions.

The first requirement for a submarine attack has always been the availability of a suitable target. Early strategists considered the submarine a defensive warship which would lie in wait and let enemy ships come to it. Therefore, no search was necessary. But in 1914, the submarine emerged as a great offensive weapon. Not content to lurk in home waters waiting for the British Grand Fleet, the German U-boats went on the prowl, and the new offensive mission gave rise to the concept of the submarine as a hunter as well as a killer lying in ambush.

Search procedures first began with the equipment available at the time: the human eye and the periscope. Later, scientific progress made other search equipment available—radar and sonar—and with those electronic eyes and ears the submarine expanded its range of detection, in darkness as well as in light.

Successful search leads to target contact, the first part of the operation which the submariner calls "approach and attack."

During the *contact phase* the submarine captain determines which side of the target is presented to him. This can be done by heading directly for or away from the target. If the direction of the target changes to the right, the submarine captain knows that he must be on the starboard side of the target. In submarine language, the target is said to have a *"starboard angle-on-the-bow."* Conversely, if the direction of the target changes to the left, the target is said to have a *"port angle-on-the-bow."*

As soon as he knows which way the target is going, the submarine captain starts the *approach phase.* During this phase, he maneuvers his submarine to a position from which he can fire torpedoes at the target. If the target changes course or speed, he must select a new firing position and head for it. In a daylight submerged approach, the submarine captain may raise the periscope several times for brief looks at the target. The short length of these exposures reduces the chance of detection by the enemy, and from these momentary observations the captain must determine the target's course, speed, and range. The accuracy of his estimates and the skill with which he handles his submarine are marks of his ability as an approach officer.

When the firing point has been reached, the *attack phase* begins. During this final evolution, the torpedoes are aimed and fired. Early submarines had to be pointed in the direction in which the torpedoes were to travel. Modern submarines, however, have aiming mechanisms which automatically set the torpedo gyroscopes to the right course, so that the submarine may be headed in any direction when firing.

It is important to note that the torpedo is not aimed directly at the target, unless the target happens to be stopped or headed directly toward or away from the submarine. In most circumstances the captain must lead his target, just as a duck shooter must aim ahead of a flying bird. For example, a 45-knot torpedo goes 1,500 yards in one minute, while a 15-knot ship goes 500 yards in the same time. Therefore, a 45-knot torpedo fired at a ship 1,500 yards away which is moving at 15 knots must be aimed 500 yards ahead of the ship in order to intercept at the proper point and score a hit.

Modern submarines have automatic computing equipment to solve the torpedo aiming problem. This equipment is a kind of electronic brain which, by performing complicated mathematical calculations in a split second, continuously computes the correct course for a torpedo to hit a moving target. It sends the correct course signal to a mechanism which sets the torpedo gyroscope. When the torpedo is fired, the gyroscope causes it to turn to the correct course and then steer along a straight path.

On a dark night the attack phase involves different tactics since the target is not visible through the periscope. Under those conditions, World War II submarines remained on the surface throughout the approach and successfully attacked their targets. American submarines made their first three attacks against Japanese ships in that manner, and in the early months of the war our submariners depended entirely on their eyesight during a night attack. Their

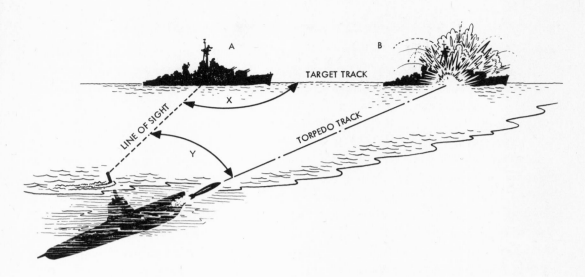

A submarine aims and fires a torpedo at a moving ship. A, *Target at time torpedo is fired.* B, *Target at time torpedo strikes.* X, *Angle-on-the-bow.* Y, *Lead angle.*

eyes were aided by the excellent light-gathering qualities of binoculars which magnified a target to seven times its normal apparent size.

The success of German wolf-pack tactics in World War II also depended on the ability of the U-boats to conduct approaches on the surface. U-boats had much greater speed on the surface than they had submerged. A pack would spread out over a convoy route and the first U-boat to spot an Allied convoy reported the position, course, and speed to the German High Command ashore. The High Command sent out signals calling all available U-boats to the scene. When a strong force of submarines had assembled, High Command sent the signal to attack. Once that signal was given, the U-boats operated independently in attacking the ships in convoy.

In that manner, a pack of ten boats operating in co-ordination with strong German air forces made the run to North Russia a hell in ice for an Allied convoy in the summer of 1942. Convoy PQ-17, thirty-four merchant ships and twenty-one escorts, left Iceland on June 27th with a load of tanks and aircraft for Russia. A covering force of four cruisers plus nine destroyers and corvettes followed on July 1st.

News that the German battleship *Tirpitz* was on the prowl led to the withdrawal of the covering force on July 4th. It later turned out that *Tirpitz* had left her berth in a Norwegian fiord for a few hours; then, unable to hide in the open sea like the U-boats, she had returned to her sanctuary.

But when the covering force withdrew its protection, the convoy scattered. The next day the merchantmen began to be picked off. A U-boat sank the freighter *Carlton*, loaded with tanks for the Russian Army. After a long surface chase at 16 knots, *U-255* got in position ahead of a large ship, submerged, and fired a salvo of torpedoes as the ship came by. Two hits sank the American ship *Alcoa Ranger*. Later, *U-255* torpedoed *Olopana*, then surfaced and sank that ship with gunfire. Other U-boats and aircraft attacked helpless, lonesome merchantmen until only eleven remained to reach Archangel. Over 130,000 tons of arms destined for the fighting front ended at the bottom of the Barents Sea.

In mid-1942, surface-search radar was introduced into United States submarines in the Pacific and that equipment completely changed night surface approach tactics. By 1944, all United States fleet-type submarines had surface-search radars. With electronic eyes that could see on the darkest night, the submarines came to the surface where their full Diesel-powered speed could be used to run down Japanese convoys. In 1944, they made over half of all their attacks on the surface rather than submerged.

By July 1944, the Japanese had withdrawn their sea forces into interior lines extending from the Empire to the Philippines and Southeast Asia. Their ability to continue the war depended on keeping those lines open and they

Venturer, *British winner of a submerged encounter with a German U-boat.*

accordingly concentrated their efforts on getting fewer but larger convoys through the American gantlet. The Japanese put all of their available destroyers and escort craft into the breach to guard those vital merchant convoys. The Americans countered by sending their submarines out in small groups, or wolf packs, in order to concentrate the maximum power on the convoys.

British submarines were credited with sinking eighteen German U-boats in World War I, but at the end of the war they were relegated to the passive role of playing target for surface ships practicing antisubmarine tactics. Their work in sinking enemy submarines was largely forgotten or discounted. Hence, they started World War II without special preparations for the task. Nevertheless, in that second conflict British submarines sank forty enemy undersea craft.

The British submarines were shrewdly and skillfully handled. Nothing exemplifies that better than an attack made by *Venturer,* under command of Lieutenant J. S. Launders. On the morning of February 9, 1945, he heard very faint noises on *Venturer's* listening sonar. Over an hour later, the watch officer momentarily sighted a periscope on the same bearing as the noise. The noise grew louder. For two hours Launders warily pursued his game, with only another glimpse of a periscope and a sound bearing here and there to guide him. He plotted the enemy's track so well from that meager information that he was able to maneuver *Venturer* undetected into position for firing torpedoes. *Venturer's* torpedoes struck the submerged target and exploded. Subsequent information indicated that the victim was *U-864,* en route back to her home port in Germany.

From start to finish, both submarines had remained submerged.

Like the British, United States submarine crews in World War II were not specially trained to fight other submarines. But they did sink twenty-five of them. In fact, the first enemy warship ever sunk by a United States submarine was a Japanese submarine.

On January 27, 1942, *Gudgeon,* commanded by Lieutenant Commander E. W. Grenfell, was running submerged near Midway Island. At 9:00 A.M., *Gudgeon's* sonar detected the sound of a ship's propellers. The watch officer turned the periscope to the sound bearing and saw a Japanese I-class submarine running fast on the surface.

Battle stations torpedo! Grenfell took the periscope and got a set-up on the enemy submarine. He called out his estimates of angle-on-the-bow and range. The gunnery officer fed them into the torpedo data computer.

Minutes later Grenfell took another look, "Enemy speed, fifteen knots."

At 9:07 A.M., computer solution tracking perfectly, range 1,800 yards, he gave the order: "Final bearing and shoot. Up periscope!"

"Bearing——mark! Fire!" Three torpedoes sped away. The sonar man heard two torpedoes explode. The propeller noises stopped. Grenfell raised the periscope and took another look. The submarine had disappeared.

The Japanese submarine *I-173* was lost in that locality on that day.

In 1914, the Russian Imperial Navy had only twenty-two old submarines, and the Russian submarine force sank only six ships during World War I. But after the war the Russian attitude toward submarines underwent a revolution along with other things in that country. The Soviet Navy had a total of one hundred sixty-five submarines at the outbreak of World War II. They claimed sinking 3,600,000 tons of enemy ships in that conflict, although not all of that amount was confirmed.

During World War II the British Navy sent some submarines to Murmansk to operate with the Soviet submarine forces. The British considered the submarine men to be the elite of the Soviet Navy, and reported that their ships were handled with great daring. Soviet officers were quick to learn British tactics and operating methods.

Since World War II the Soviets have launched the greatest submarine-building program in history. Included in that program are many W-class submarines, with a long cruising range and a reported speed of 17 knots surfaced and 13 knots submerged. In 1958, they were near the halfway mark toward their goal of twelve hundred submarines.

Russian submarine in the San Francisco area. This World War II Soviet submarine was photographed during its visit to Mare Island Navy Yard, California.

These Russian W-class submarines are the most modern seagoing types in the Soviet undersea fleet. The bottom picture, released by the United States Navy in December 1957, was taken by a Navy reconnaissance plane while on Atlantic patrol.

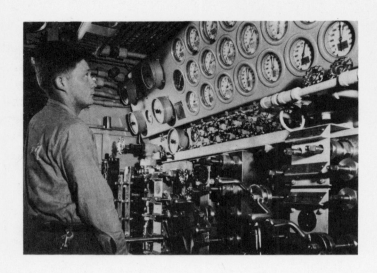

9. *Men Against Pressure*

SUBMARINERS ordinarily count upon not only diving in their ships, but also upon returning to the surface. It occasionally happens, however, that it doesn't work out that way. Like any other ship, a submarine can be sunk. If the accident causing the sinking takes place when the vessel is submerged, the crew takes action to restore positive buoyancy. Should these measures fail, those aboard must either be rescued by outside means or else take advantage of escape measures which have been developed to a high degree of reliability.

Early designers in the submarine field devoted their attentions to creating craft which were capable of ever-increasing operational efficiency. They gave little or no attention to provisions for survival of the crew in the event of disaster, and only when tragedy had struck several times was effective recognition given to that phase of the submarine problem. Significantly, it was the United States Navy which first showed major interest and took effective action. Our country has never, even in the dangerous business of war machines and their use, been able to ignore the safety of those who must perform the dangerous work involved. Yet even we were slow in initiating corrective measures to take care of submarine disasters. Escape from a submarine was to remain for some time a matter of coming up with the boat or not coming up at all. The tragedy of *S-4* gave poignant emphasis to the situation.

S-4 sank off Provincetown, Massachusetts, on December 17, 1927, after a collision with the Coast Guard destroyer *Paulding*. A diver who was rushed to the scene found the ship lying in 102 feet of water. Signaling by tapping the hull, he found that there were six men alive in the torpedo room forward. Elsewhere the ship was ominously silent. Air lines from surface ships were coupled on in an attempt to blow the water from the ballast tanks. When this failed, pontoons were positioned over the wreck for an attempt to raise it. Foul weather blew in and stopped all work.

Three months later, *S-4* was brought to the surface.

All dead.

It was after this disaster that Navy and civilian scientists set about devising ways to save those trapped in submarines. The work begun by a special commission called by the Secretary of the Navy in 1928, has been carried on by the Navy through the years. Devices have been developed to effect the rescue of trapped submariners by outside means, and other inventions, coupled with modifications of the submarine structure, enable the crew to get themselves out.

One of the major problems in helping a sunken submarine is to locate it. The very advantage of self-concealment that makes the submarine uniquely effective as a warship also makes it difficult to find in time of disaster. But measures have now been put into effect to counter that difficulty.

A bright-yellow marker buoy is fixed to the topside of United States submarines. Releasable from inside the craft, it floats to the surface carrying with it a telephone line. A plate attached to the buoy states the identity of the submarine and the fact that a telephone is inside.

In addition, submarines are fitted with means of firing emergency signals while submerged. These signals create brightly colored pyrotechnics above the water.

Finally, it is a requirement in peacetime that our submarines report by radio before commencing a dive. They give their location, their proposed course and speed while submerged, and the time they plan to surface. If that time passes with no report, search and rescue operations are commenced immediately. With such provisions for communicating, a sunken submarine has a good chance of being located promptly.

None of these steps, however, can be taken in wartime. The buoy could be jarred loose by a depth charge, giving the enemy a precise aiming point for his attack. Firing a distress signal would provide the enemy with the same information, and his response would be to keep blasting away. In wartime, submarines could not report diving plans by radio, because an enemy would use his direction finders on any transmission and quickly pinpoint the submarine's position for an attack.

The most successful means of releasing trapped personnel is the rescue chamber, the major piece of rescue equipment carried aboard every Submarine Salvage Ship (ASR). One salvage ship is stationed in every area of extensive submarine operations.

The rescue chamber itself is a steel cylinder designed to withstand the max-

The salvage ship U.S.S. Chanticleer *is equipped to bring up survivors from a sunken submarine. The rescue chamber is on the port side abaft the superstructure.*

imum depths which a submarine pressure hull is capable of resisting. It is 11 feet tall, 7 feet in diameter and weighs about 10 tons. It is divided into three major parts: the upper compartment, the lower compartment, and the main ballast tank which surrounds the lower compartment. The lower compartment and the main ballast tanks are fitted with floods and vents so that they can be filled or emptied from the sea in the same manner as the main ballast tanks of a submarine.

The rescue chamber is carried on the deck of the salvage vessel, and lowered into the sea by means of a crane at the stern of the ship. A telephone line maintains communication with the ship. One air line provides a supply of high-pressure air from the ship's compressors, another permits the bell to vent air to the surface. A waterproof cable provides lighting current.

The upper compartment is fitted with a hatch at the top to permit operating personnel to enter after it has been lowered over the side to deck level. A hatch at the bottom of the upper compartment leads to the lower chamber. Within the upper compartment is space for the two operators and six rescued passengers.

The rescue chamber's rise and descent are controlled by means of a reel within the lower compartment driven by a compressed-air motor. The reel takes a strain on the submarine's messenger cable (the one which was carried to the surface by the bright-yellow marker buoy) in order to drag the rescue chamber downward. Reversing the direction of the reel eases the strain, and the rescue chamber rises because of its own positive buoyancy.

The rescue chamber operator controls the flooding of the device so as to maintain about 1,000 pounds of positive buoyancy, which keeps the messenger cable taut to avoid tangling. If the cable should become tangled, he floods to bring about negative buoyancy, cuts the cable, and the chamber is hauled to the surface by the rescue ship's crane. Were he just to cut the cable, the chamber would bob to the surface as a result of positive buoyancy; but it might well hit the underside of the rescue vessel with fatal results to the chamber occupants.

The crane operator on the rescue ship keeps just enough strain on his "backhaul" cable to the rescue chamber to avoid entanglement as the chamber rises or descends. Only in the emergency condition of a fouled downhaul cable would the crane operator attempt to control the depth of the chamber, in which case he would haul it back to the surface.

Now, let us follow a typical rescue operation. When the rescue chamber makes contact with the submarine and is precisely positioned, the chamber's ballast tank is flooded. The rescue chamber now has negative buoyancy of

Crewmen enter the upper compartment of a rescue chamber prior to its descent.

3,000 pounds and rests tightly against the submarine. Water is then blown from the lower chamber by compressed air. When it is empty the flood valves through which the water was blown out are closed, and the air pressure within the bell is reduced to atmospheric level.

The rescue chamber is now sealed firmly against the submarine by the difference in pressure between the low pressure of air inside and the high pressure of water outside. It is much the same as a rubber suction cup with low pressure inside, being held against a smooth surface by atmospheric pressure.

With the chamber secured to the deck, the submarine's escape hatch is cautiously opened. The reason for caution is that flooding of part of the submarine or use of her compressed air in attempts to expel water may have built up relatively high pressure within the boat. The sudden release of such pressure could cause injury to men's lungs or eardrums.

With pressure between chamber and hull equalized at atmospheric pressure, the first six of the trapped men are taken into the upper compartment of the chamber. The submarine hatch is closed securely, the chamber's ballast tanks are blown, and the air motor reels out the messenger cable to permit the chamber and its passengers to rise to the surface by its own positive buoyancy.

The rescue chamber is the most successful means of getting men out of a sunken submarine. It requires no special training on the part of those rescued, and it requires no effort on the part of men who may be in poor physical or mental condition as a result of long entrapment. It subjects the men to none of the dangers always present when the human body is subjected to the pressure of deep water, since the pressure of the air within the rescue chamber is always the same as that at the surface.

The rescue chamber first demonstrated its worth when it was used on the sunken *Squalus* in 1939. Every man who survived the immediate flooding of the submarine was safely brought to the surface.

Although the rescue chamber is beyond doubt the best means of bringing submarine survivors to the surface, it is not always possible to use it. The submarine may have been sunk in a spot so distant from the nearest salvage ship that men would die from asphyxiation before the chamber could be brought to the scene. Also, the sea conditions at the surface may be so adverse that the rescue ship could not make and maintain the precise mooring in time to get the men out. And finally, there is still the possibility that the submarine, despite all measures to assure locating it, might not be found in time, as, for example, under prolonged stormy or foggy conditions.

To give those within the sunken submarine a good chance of survival even in the absence of a rescue chamber operation, means have been devised for individual escape.

The decision to use the individual escape technique must be made by the senior survivor within the submarine. He must make his decision promptly, because prolonged fouling of the air can cause men to become so ill that they

U.S.S. Squalus. *When she sank off Portsmouth, New Hampshire, in 1939, a rescue chamber saved her crew, the first time a rescue chamber had ever been used.*

are physically unable to save themselves or mentally deprived of the will to live. The decision must take into account many factors. Is it possible that a suitably equipped salvage ship can reach the scene in time? Is it the right time to escape individually? It would do no good to have swimmers get to the surface in darkness when chances of being picked up are poor. Are there ships in the vicinity to pick up the men? The telephone line from the emergency buoy, if working, could confirm their presence, or the submarine's own listening gear, if not damaged, would pick up surface ship noise. These are all important questions, for in parts of the ocean where the water is very cold men would not survive unless picked up promptly by ships in the immediate vicinity when escape is made.

The methods of individual escape are quite satisfactory for most persons down to depths of about 300 feet. But the procedures must be precisely followed. Death, masked in subtle initial symptoms, quickly takes for its own the man who does not do exactly what is prescribed.

The first major contribution to individual escape technique was the Momsen Lung perfected in 1929 by Lieutenant Charles B. Momsen, Chief Gunner C. L. Tibbals, and Mr. Frank M. Hobson, a Navy civilian employee. It was a mouth mask connected by a large flexible tube to a bag containing oxygen and an absorbent for removal of carbon dioxide. The volume of oxygen held by the Lung was a little over a gallon. It was more than adequate for a slow ascent from any safe depth.

To make possible individual escape using the Momsen Lung, designers had to provide for a means of getting out of the submarine without flooding it. In fleet-type submarines, escape exits were provided in both the forward and the after part of the ship.

The forward exit, located in the forward torpedo room, consisted of a chamber mounted in the superstructure. A lower hatch provided entry from the pressure hull while a side hatch permitted exit to the sea through an opening in the superstructure. Controls within the chamber provided for admitting compressed air and sea water as necessary to effect escape. The chamber could hold four men at a time.

The escapees, carrying Momsen Lungs, entered the chamber from the pressure hull through the lower hatch. When that hatch was closed, the man opened a valve to admit sea water until the pressure inside the chamber equaled the sea pressure outside. Air was then admitted from the ship's supply line to lower the depth of the water to the top of the side door. The men then charged their Lungs and the door was opened.

In turn, the men seized hold of the messenger cable which had been run up to the surface with the emergency buoy. To assure maintenance of an upright stance, the escapee clamped the line between his feet. Rate of ascent was controlled by the braking action of the hands on the line.

A slow rate of ascent was essential to successful escape. Should the escapee yield to the impulse to get to the surface as rapidly as possible, he could fatally injure himself through the occurrence of what medical men call an "air embolism." The sequence of events culminating in an air embolism starts with the overexpansion of the lungs. This results when the high-pressure air breathed in at the start of the ascent expands the lungs as the water pressure drops during the course of ascent. The lungs are ruptured and bubbles of air are forced into the blood stream. When a bubble reaches the heart, that vital organ loses suction, just as an air bubble will cause a water pump to lose "prime." The heart then stops pumping, and the results are well known.

Following development of the Momsen Lung, the British brought out the Davis gear, and the Germans introduced the Draeger equipment. Each features a face mask and air-supply bag. In addition, they contain extra oxygen bottles which extend the time that may be spent under water. The Davis device includes an apronlike attachment which, held out horizontally, retards the speed of ascent and substitutes for the ascending line of the Momsen Lung.

In 1946, the British Submarine Escape Committee, established by the Admiralty to devise ways of helping trapped submariners, made an interesting statistical discovery. The Committee found that for every two successful escapes made with the latest devices available, there were three successful escapes without any assistance from escape apparatus. The finding suggested that perhaps the fewer the gadgets the less chance there was to have something go wrong.

Experiments disclosed that the individual could do a very nice job of ascending from a sunken submarine armed only with the lungs that nature provided him and some useful information. The useful information was the requirement that, come what may, he must continuously exhale all the way to the surface.

The method, known as free-buoyancy escape, works this way. When the

Candidates at the Submarine School learning how to use the Momsen Lung when escaping from a disabled submarine. They practice here in a 100-foot water tank.

escape trunk or chamber has been properly rigged for use as in the Momsen Lung procedure, the free-buoyancy escapee takes some deliberate deep breaths. These inhalations not only fill his lungs but also give a maximum charge of oxygen to his blood stream.

Then he ducks out the hatch and lets his inherent free buoyancy take him to the surface.

As in the case of the Momsen Lung method, the need is paramount to equalize pressure constantly between the lungs and the outside water pressure to avoid air embolism. To do that requires that the escapee slowly and continuously exhale air all the way to the surface, a maneuver which takes a bit of doing, because the absence of any replacement source of air naturally inclines the escapee to hold his breath. But if he does hold his breath, he will explode his lungs and die.

An ascent from deep water takes a long time. It might appear that the escapee by constantly exhaling would run out of air before he reaches the surface. Actually, there is little danger of that. The air driven into his blood stream at high pressure when he started his ascent is trying to escape as the pressure against his body is reduced incident to ascending to shallower water. Nature's escape route for the trapped air is into the lungs and out through the mouth.

Nature knows best, and the man will do well just to let the air flow out continuously as he rises. The supply in his lungs will be renewed from the blood.

The free-buoyancy escape technique was subjected to careful investigation by the United States Navy and proved to be completely satisfactory. In 1957, the use of Momsen Lungs was discontinued, and today the free-buoyancy method is the standard alternative to escape by means of the rescue chamber. Momsen Lungs are no longer carried aboard our submarines. The escape exits used when the Momsen Lung was standard equipment are well suited to the free-buoyancy method and remain structural features in modern undersea craft of our Navy.

The free-buoyancy escape method, however, is not without peril. If made without an ascending line, it can result in the escapee becoming directionally confused and trying to head downward instead of toward the surface. The ascending line serves as a means of directional reference. One way of avoiding such dangerous confusion is for the escapee to watch the air bubbles of his continuous exhalation during ascent. Air always rises. But poor visibility in deep water can prevent a man from even seeing the bubbles. A better solution to directional trouble is for a man to carry a buoyant object in his hand. It will tend to lift the hand and thus point the way to the surface.

Frequently the suggestion is made that the ready solution for the directional confusion problem would be for the escapee to wear a conventional life jacket. But that has a serious disadvantage in that it would greatly accelerate his rate of ascent with dangerously increased hazard of air embolism. He could exhale at a faster rate, but there is a limit to the rapidity with which air can be expelled through the respiratory channels. It might not be equal to the requirement for an ascent boosted by a life jacket.

Whatever technique is employed to escape from a sunken submarine, success depends upon doing precisely the right thing at the right time. The clear thinking essential to such precision can be reasonably assured only by intensive training.

At the submarine bases in New London, Connecticut, and Pearl Harbor there are 100-foot cylindrical water tanks that provide training for all escape techniques. At the bottom of the tanks are compartments with hatches that simulate the hull of a submarine. A miniature rescue chamber is lowered into place over the hatch to provide training in the transfer procedure from a sunken craft to the rescue chamber. In addition, the towers are provided with means of entry at various levels. Starting at the shallowest, men are trained in the free-buoyancy escape technique. As their state of training advances, they descend to greater depths.

There is always the chance of disaster in a submarine, but our Navy does its best to give those involved an ever-increasing margin favoring survival. New devices, new techniques, and continuous training lead to the attainment of greater safety.

A long way up. At the submarine base in New London, Connecticut, this 100-foot cylindrical water tank provides training for all escape techniques.

10. *Odd Ones*

AFTER THE SUBMARINE had finally evolved into a war vessel accepted by the principal sea powers, new and unusual applications brought about unorthodox submersibles, such as midget submarines, manned torpedoes, and sphere-shaped tanks. The tanks were built not for military purposes, but to explore extreme depths in scientific research projects.

The largest category of submerging oddities is that represented by the midget submarine. The midgets were designed principally for sneak attacks in restricted enemy waters, such as protected harbors and approaches to rivers. Such target situations are usually of a nature which preclude the use of conventional submarines.

One of the most successful midget submarine attacks was that made against the German battleship *Tirpitz* in September 1943. The powerful *Tirpitz* with her 15-inch guns, heavy armor plating, and great speed, posed a terrible threat to allied convoys on the northern route to Russia, known as the Murmansk run. She could raid the slow allied convoys, and inflict great losses in ships, cargo, and most important of all, men.

From her hide-out in Kaa Fiord, *Tirpitz* was relatively safe from air attack. Since the Fiord lies deep within the sheer cliffs of the Norwegian coast, aircraft torpedo attacks were impossible, and bombing attacks most difficult. *Tirpitz* was protected by strategically placed antiaircraft batteries, supplementing her own heavy firepower, a triple cordon of antitorpedo nets around the ship, another net across the entrance of the Fiord, mine fields to seaward, and patrols guarding the approaches.

To solve this formidable target problem, special submarines, the British X-craft, were designed. The X-craft were only 48 feet in length. They were propelled on the surface by Diesel power, and ran submerged on a battery-driven electric motor. Being short-ranged, they had to be towed to within striking distance of their targets. For armament, two releasable explosive charges were carried outboard. Two officers and two enlisted ratings comprised the crew.

On September 11, 1943, six X-craft departed Loch Cairnbawn, Scotland, for attacks on enemy targets in the Norwegian fiords. Three of the midgets, *X-5, X-6,* and *X-7,* were designated to attack *Tirpitz.* On the night of September 20th, the midget submarines slipped their towlines off the Norwegian coast. After crossing over the mine fields on the surface, the X-craft submerged at dawn and reached Alten Fiord by dusk on the 21st. Hiding in the Brattholm group of islands, in the Fiord, the midgets recharged their batteries for the final run into Kaa Fiord, where the German battleship was moored behind the protective nets, 4 miles away.

First into Kaa Fiord was *X-6,* under command of Lieutenant Donald Cameron. She passed through a gap in the torpedo net at the head of the Fiord at five o'clock in the morning. At this point, however, *X-6* suffered the first of a series of mishaps in her dangerous mission; her periscope flooded.

Designed for sneak attacks in harbors and rivers, British X-craft were midget submarines which attacked shipping in both European waters and the Far East.

After making emergency repairs, the crew brought her up to periscope depth again and found themselves close to the boat gap in the first of the antitorpedo nets surrounding *Tirpitz*. By 7:05 A.M., running submerged, *X-6* was through the nets and within 200 yards of the *Tirpitz*, but then the periscope flooded again. Temporarily blinded, *X-6* ran aground and broke surface. Miraculously escaping detection on *Tirpitz*, she managed to float free and resumed her approach to her target. But within a few minutes, she broke surface again and this time was sighted by the lookouts.

Still unable to use his periscope, Cameron submerged and steered blindly for the big warship. *X-6* blundered into the nets, broke free, and then bobbed to the surface again. The luckless submarine drew a hail of rifle fire and hand grenades. With the element of surprise gone, and still continuing blindly, Cameron brought *X-6* so close to *Tirpitz* that he scraped her hull. With capture imminent, Cameron destroyed secret equipment, released his two explosive charges, and scuttled *X-6* near *Tirpitz*. One of *Tirpitz's* small boats came along just as *X-6* began to sink and the four-man crew was captured and taken aboard the battleship.

Lieutenant Place, skippering *X-7*, was the next to make an attack. Unable to find gaps in the nets, Place tried to pass underneath them but he found that the German nets extended all the way to the bottom of the Fiord. *X-7* repeatedly became entangled in the nets. However, by backing and going ahead, Place eventually worked his way into position for a clear approach to his target with no intervening nets. While going ahead submerged, he struck the port side of the ship and slid under. There he dropped his two charges about 175 feet apart beneath the keel.

His mission accomplished, Place began the hazardous task of getting away. His compass was out of order as a result of the shock of collision with *Tirpitz*, and Place had no idea of what course he was taking at any time. But he carried on blindly—for the very good reason that each minute brought nearer the instant when the charges he had planted under *Tirpitz* would explode. For an agonizing hour, *X-7* struggled free of one net entanglement after another. Finally, Place surfaced to slide over the nets. Promptly *Tirpitz* machine-gunners opened fire.

Once again, *X-7* dove for the protective depths and once more she became enmeshed in a net. At 8:12 A.M., a great explosion shook *X-7* out of the net, and her skipper took her deep to contemplate his situation. But damage suffered from the explosion made it impossible to maintain *X-7* at any selected depth. She kept rising to the surface, and at each surfacing she was subjected to more enemy fire. Finally, Place scuttled his ship and escaped with only one of his crew. They were later captured.

Aboard the *Tirpitz*, the captain realized that he was being attacked by submarines, and guessed that they were planting timed charges. He ordered the forward starboard mooring cable heaved in, to warp the ship away from the spot where he estimated the charges had been planted. Although this moved the ship's bow approximately 50 yards from her previous position, and away from three of the four charges, it left the ship so placed that one of the 2-ton charges from *X-7* was directly under the engine room. Aboard *Tirpitz,* four men knew that the ship still lay above a grimly ticking piece of sudden death. They were Cameron and his crew captured from *X-6.* They didn't talk. At 8:12 A.M. (Greenwich mean time) the 2-ton weapon went off. *Tirpitz's* stern heaved 6 feet out of the water. Crew members were flung from the weather deck into the air. The main engines were put out of action and 500 tons of water flooded her compartments.

During the excitement and confusion of the explosion, a third X-craft was sighted about 500 yards from *Tirpitz* at 8:30 A.M. This was undoubtedly the hapless *X-5,* approaching a stirred-up hornets' nest. She was fired upon by *Tirpitz* and sank outside the nets. Destroyers dropped depth charges where *X-5* disappeared. There were no survivors.

Tirpitz was not sunk, but she never again figured as an offensive threat in World War II.

Of the six X-craft which started out from Loch Cairnbawn, none returned. *X-8* had to be scuttled when mechanical trouble threatened to compromise her scheduled attack against the cruiser *Lutzow. X-9* was lost without trace when her towline parted in the North Sea. *X-10* penetrated Alten Fiord to attack the battleship *Scharnhorst.* However, that ship was at sea on gunnery exercises, and stayed clear of Alten Fiord when warned by radio from *Tirpitz* of the local situation. *X-10* jettisoned her two charges and although she managed to regain contact with a towing submarine five days later, she succumbed to heavy weather and was lost at sea after her crew was removed.

Japanese midget submarines were introduced early in World War II, even arriving off the entrance to Pearl Harbor before the war started. The Pearl Harbor attack provided the Japanese submarines with an ideal target situation—assault on a base of a country not at war. This is the ultimate in surprise. The failure of the Japanese midget submarine attack on Pearl Harbor was indicative of lack of skill in the use of submarines—a failing that characterized their submarine campaign in World War II.

The Japanese midget submarines of the type which joined the attack at Pearl Harbor were built in the navy yard at Kure. The first two appeared in 1934 and by 1943, sixty-two had been completed. Those midget submarines were cigar-shaped craft 78 feet in length, and 6 feet in diameter. The electric motors used for both surfaced and submerged running gave them a top speed of 19 knots, at which speed the batteries would be completely exhausted in fifty minutes. They carried two torpedoes internally, mounted one over the other. They could be transported on board a seaplane tender or on the deck of large submarines. For the attack on Pearl Harbor, five of these midgets were carried on I-16 type submarines. The mother submarines arrived with their papooses—rigged midgets—on the night of December 6, 1941, and lay to in the moonlit Hawaiian waters, awaiting an early-morning launching.

The first midget submarine was sighted at 3:42 A.M. approaching the harbor entrance by the mine sweeper U.S.S. *Condor*. The contact was passed to the destroyer U.S.S. *Ward,* but this submarine managed to slip through the antisubmarine net undetected.

It was about 6:30 A.M. when the U.S.S. *Antares* reported seeing another small submarine in the approaches to the entrance of Pearl Harbor. *Ward* was asked to investigate. With the help of a Navy patrol plane which dropped two smoke pots to mark the submarine's position, *Ward* spotted the submarine and attacked. Two shots were fired at close range.

The second hit the midget submarine just at the base of the conning tower. The sub heeled over momentarily but continued coming on into the wake of the destroyer. Four depth charges were rolled off *Ward's* stern. The first one was apparently enough. As the eruption of water and spray settled back to the surface, the submarine went down and oil came up. It was the end of a bold try.

Meanwhile the first sub sighted had entered the harbor. She fired both of her torpedoes and with better luck she might have had some success. But one torpedo beached itself in the mud of Ford Island, after first passing between the light cruiser *Raleigh* and the seaplane tender *Curtiss*. The other torpedo nosed into the mud in battleship row. The midget submarine, after

Disaster was routine for Japanese midget submarines at Pearl Harbor. This one beached off Bellows Field, and her skipper became the first Japanese prisoner of war in World War II.

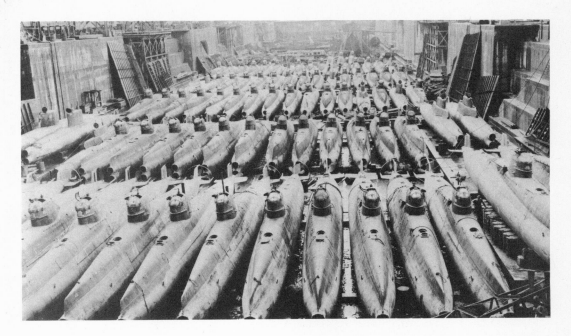

These craft were never launched. Spawned too late for combat in World War II, row upon row of midget submarines cram the Naval Base at Kure, Japan.

drawing fire from a number of ships, was depth-charged by the destroyer *Monaghan*. A shallow depth charge set at 30 feet completely smashed the craft. The mangled remains were later recovered from the harbor bottom, and after a military funeral for its personnel, the hulk was used as fill for a new pier.

The third midget submarine was her own worst enemy, for she almost asphyxiated her two-man crew. She had drifted around to the windward side of the island of Oahu, finally got hung up on a reef, and later beached herself off Bellows Field, an Army Air Force base. After setting a demolition charge, the skipper and his assistant tried to swim ashore. To top off a series of failures, neither one of these operations was successful. The demolition charge failed to detonate, and the assistant drowned before reaching the beach. The surf washed the skipper up on the beach unconscious, and he shortly afterward had the dubious distinction of becoming the first Japanese prisoner of war in World War II.

Recognizing the possible value of midget submarines for special assignments, the United States in 1956 began testing a small submarine called *X-1*. Less than 40 feet in length, this type submarine holds promise for a variety of special missions.

As the long-range submarine grows larger to accomplish an ever-increasing variety of missions and tasks, there may well emerge as an important naval defense craft, a small, high-speed submarine to counter the larger submarine just as the small, high-speed fighter plane was required to fight the heavy bomber of the mid-twentieth century.

The long and short of it. An experimental midget measures up to U.S.S. Bergall.

A small submersible may be purchased commercially for recreational use. It is the Aerojet Minisub. It measures 172 inches in length and 22 inches in breadth, and is propelled by foot pedals or by an electric motor run on batteries. Maneuvering is accomplished by a single control wheel which moves control surfaces similar to those of an airplane.

Prior to the entry of the United States into World War I, Germany tried to break the British blockade by using cargo submarines to bring critically needed materials from the United States. One such craft, *Deutschland,* made two successful round trips between Germany and our east coast. The second cargo submarine, *Bremen,* was captured by the British on her initial voyage. But the United States came into the war before Germany could further exploit the cargo submarine concept, and no serious attention was given the idea for more than forty years.

In World War II, Japan was forced to use combatant submarines as cargo carriers for communicating with Germany. They took tin and rubber for the hard-pressed German industrial machine and were to bring back optical goods and other items scarce in Japan. Of five submarines which attempted the round trip from Singapore to the German-held ports in France, only one returned. The rest were destroyed by enemy action or succumbed to the rigors of the voyage.

With the end of the war, interest in the cargo capability of submarines ended, as it always had. But in January 1957, the Mitsubishi Heavy Industries Company of Japan was reported to be planning a nuclear-powered submarine tanker of 30,000 tons displacement and a submerged speed of 22 knots. The ship would be 540 feet long and have a beam of 69 feet. In 1958, it was revealed that the company had a scale model, 9 meters in length and displacing 2 tons, which was being sailed in sheltered waters to test the effectiveness of hull configuration for the new tanker.

Shortly after announcement of the Japanese interest in construction of a commercial submarine tanker, it was revealed that the British marine designers, Mitchell Engineering Company, were making tests of small models of a submarine tanker which, in the words of a company official, "might be as big as 100,000 tons."

In February 1958, the United States Department of Commerce announced the award of a contract to the Electric Boat Division of General Dynamics Corporation to study the feasibility of constructing a submarine tanker. The announcement stated that such vessels would "offer reduced resistance at high speeds in comparison with surface ships and could maintain scheduled speeds without regard to surface conditions."

The submarine was gaining recognition as a major asset to commerce.

Conventional submarines, being limited to a submergence depth of a few hundred feet, are unsuitable for probing the mysteries of the great ocean depths which for centuries caused man to wonder and conjecture. The design breakthrough which provided a partial solution to that problem came in 1934, when William Beebe and Otis Barton succeeded in descending to 3,028 feet in a bathysphere, a steel sphere suspended from a cable.

In the late thirties, Auguste Piccard commenced construction of a self-propelled craft for deep-sea observation. He called it a bathyscaphe. The war interrupted the venture, but it was resumed after the end of hostilities. The first bathyscaphe was completed in 1948, and tested to a depth of 12,000 feet without any form of suspension from the surface. In 1950, the bathyscaphe,

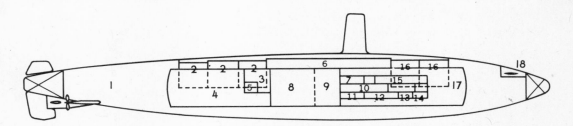

Proposed nuclear-powered Japanese submarine tanker. 1, 4, 6, 17: *Cargo oil tanks.* 2, 16: *Ballast tanks.* 3, 12: *Auxiliary machinery spaces.* 5, 14: *Trim tanks.* 8: *Engine room.* 9: *Reactor room.* 10: *Crew's quarters.* 11: *Battery room.* 13: *Stowage space.* 15: *Wardroom.* 18: *Diving plane. Specifications: Length, 180 meters; beam, 23 meters; cargo capacity, 30,000 tons; submerged speed, 22 knots; shaft horsepower, 40,000; main drive, two steam turbines; one nuclear reactor.*

designated *FNRS-2,* was turned over to the French Navy, and after the French Navy built a new flotation hull designed to withstand the rough seas and long tows, the craft proved successful in deep-sea dives.

Auguste Piccard and his son, Jacques, built the bathyscaphe *Trieste* in 1952–1953. The 10-ton *Trieste* was larger than her predecessor, with enough room to accommodate four persons, but both bathyscaphes were similar in basic design.

The bathyscaphe consisted of two major parts; the sphere and the float. The sphere carried the pilot and observers, while the attached float provided the necessary buoyancy at any depth. The sphere and float were permanently attached to each other. The sphere was built of high-test, forged steel, and was able to withstand sea water pressure at a depth of 9 miles—deeper than the greatest known ocean depth. Similar construction of the float, however, would have made the device prohibitively heavy.

To construct a float of light material yet able to withstand extreme pressure was the problem confronting the Piccards. The large size of the float required that it be made of light material, but if such a float were filled with any kind of gas it would collapse at deep sea pressures because gases are compressible.

Smooth, silent, and efficient, the submarine tanker of the future speeds ahead of her surface sister ship in this artist's conception of the vessel being developed by British Engineering Company. The absence of a bow wave gives the submarine significant advantage in speed for comparable horsepower.

Piccard's bathyscaphe Trieste *is hoisted, revealing both her sphere and float.*

Therefore some form of liquid was required to provide buoyancy. Their solution treated liquids in the same manner that balloonists had treated gases. They filled their thin-skinned float with gasoline, the lightest liquid readily available.

An opening at the bottom of the float permitted free entry of sea water in order to equalize pressure inside the float with that of the sea. Gasoline had the additional advantage of not mixing with water. Being lighter than water, it floated on top as the sea water entered or left the reservoir in response to pressure changes at varying depths.

To make the bathyscaphe sink, it was made heavier by adding water ballast. To rise, weight was lessened by releasing iron shot held in vertical hoppers by an electromagnet. As a safety measure the circuits were arranged so that any electrical breakdown would cause the release of the entire 4 tons of iron ballast, with consequences no more serious than a premature rise to the surface.

All equipment, including the propulsion motors which provided horizontal movement while the bathyscaphe was suspended in water and while on the bottom, was driven by power from storage batteries. Searchlights illuminated the area visible from the observation ports. Electronic flash-gun and photographic units, including moving-picture cameras, bottles for obtaining water samples with electromagnetic controls, and an apparatus for recording sea temperatures, provided the means for recording data in the ocean's depths.

The searchlight provided illumination sufficient for seeing at a distance of about 100 feet in clear water—adequate for deliberate scientific exploration, but far too short a distance to be of practical use in a high-speed submarine whose conning tower is more than 100 feet from the bow.

The role of bathyscaphes in the future will probably be a peaceful one of oceanographic research and possibly deep salvage work. However, knowledge of the ocean depths and the land under the sea will undoubtedly contribute substantially to the future of submarine traffic for both military and civilian purposes. It is fortunate that this new frontier below the sea is unfolding concurrently with a new era for the submarine in war and peace.

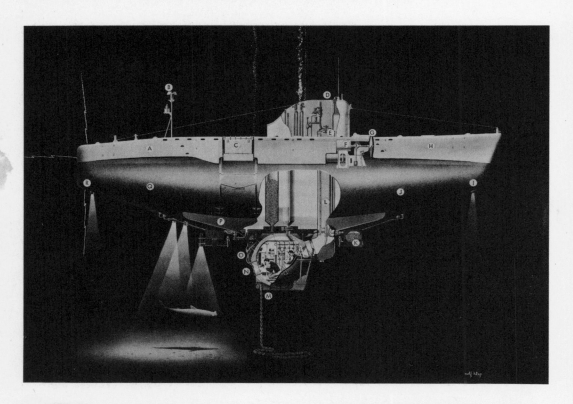

*The bathyscaphe, first device designed for free descent to extreme ocean depths.
A, After air tank. B, Vertical speed indicator. C, Batteries. D, Conning tower.
E, Hatch and air lock. F, Electric motors. G, Propellers. H, Forward air tank.
I, Bow light. J, Gasoline buoyancy tank. K, Lead shot ballast hopper. L, Air
lock access trunk. M, Guide chain for hovering above ocean floor. N, Viewing
port. O, Electronic flash gun. P, Stabilizing keel. Q, Gasoline buoyancy tank.
R, Sonic detector.* (© National Geographic Society, courtesy National
Geographic Magazine.)

11. Men for the Undersea Navy

EVEN IN THE AGE of guided missiles, automation, and push-button warfare, the human being is the most important part of any fighting force. The world's best submarine would be only a hollow steel shell unless manned by a crew of competent, trained sailors.

Not everyone can become a submariner. Because of the rugged conditions of living in a confined space for prolonged periods of time, and because submarines are complex machines that demand special skills to operate them, the United States Navy carefully selects the men who receive training for submarine duty.

All submarine sailors are volunteers—no one is drafted or conscripted for duty in undersea ships. But not all of those who volunteer are chosen. A man who is on duty in the fleet or who is completing recruit training at a naval training center, and who will remain in the Navy for two years from the time his submarine schooling begins, may request duty in submarines. First, the volunteer's Navy record is checked to see that he has above-average mechanical aptitude. Then he is given a preliminary physical examination, with special attention to his psychological adjustment and suitability for duty in submarines. Once the candidate has passed this examination, he is on his way to the Submarine School at New London, Connecticut.

When he arrives at New London, our candidate reports to the Medical Research Laboratory, where he receives a thorough going-over by submarine

Looking north over the submarine base at New London, Connecticut, where the Submarine School is located. Officers and enlisted men volunteer for training here.

medical officers. In addition to giving him a regular physical examination, they give him a special sensory test, which includes complete evaluation of eyesight, for near and distant vision and for color perception; it also includes complete hearing tests, not only for the ability to hear faint noises but also for the faculty of detecting slight differences in loudness and pitch of sounds. The latter tests are particularly important for determining whether a man has a special aptitude for becoming a sonar operator.

After these tests, our candidate, together with a group of twelve to fifteen of his fellows, is given basic training in the submarine escape tank. This training tests the candidate's adaptability to pressure changes. Also, if a man has a latent tendency toward fear and panic in enclosed spaces, it will be revealed during the tank training and he need not continue with further training.

Finally, the volunteer is interviewed by a medical officer who judges his temperamental and emotional qualities and evaluates his ability to fit into life on board a submarine. It is not necessary that the candidate be an unusual person—far from it—the normal well-balanced individual is most likely to be a good submariner. It is the basically hesitant, slow-thinking person or the wild, harebrained "screwball" who must be eliminated. For in a submarine, to a greater degree than in any other craft, the safety of all is dependent on the ability of each man to perform his job quickly and precisely under conditions of great stress.

When our candidate has passed the medical examination, he enters the

What the Submarine School candidate learns in class is later practiced in training cruises at sea. The submarine's hydraulic system is the lesson for today.

Submarine School as a student in the basic course. In that course he is given eight weeks of intensive indoctrination in the structure of submarines, the engineering plant, diving and surfacing procedures, and the high-pressure air systems, hydraulic systems, and water systems which are vital to the operation of the modern submarine. Part of this time is spent under way at sea in a submarine, so that the student can practice the knowledge that he is gaining in the classrooms.

The instructors at the Submarine School are experienced submariners, with specialized knowledge in the subjects they teach. For training they use demonstration aids—scale models of submarines that show the various piping and control systems, and full-size equipment such as torpedo tubes, engines, and maneuvering controls. One of the most important training devices is the Askania diving trainer, a dry-land counterpart of the diving controls of a submarine. The diving trainer reacts in exactly the same manner as a water-borne submarine. When the men operating the diving plane controls place them on "dive," the trainer tilts forward and the depth gauge indicates that the device is going down. To level off, the operators must put the diving planes in the correct position. In addition to plane controls, the Askania has levers and valves which are the exact duplicates of those in a submarine's control room. Operation of these levers and valves causes the machine to simulate all the sensory impressions of a person actually in a submarine in which the same mechanisms would be flooding, pumping, or blowing water into or out of the ballast tanks. The Askania diving trainer is invaluable for the indoctrination of new submarine crews—it behaves just like a live submarine, except that it doesn't leak!

At the conclusion of the eight-week course, the graduate of the Submarine School is given orders to duty aboard a submarine. Soon after he reports on board, his instruction in the "School of the Boat" begins. This is a program carried out on every submarine to help prepare new men to become qualified submariners. The new crew member learns how to rig every compartment for diving, how to man the controls for diving and surfacing, how to fire torpedoes, and how to operate all of the machinery in his submarine. When he has successfully completed the School of the Boat, the submarine sailor is officially designated "Qualified in Submarines"—he has earned his dolphins, the emblem of the submarine service. The twin-dolphin insignia, silver for enlisted men or gold for officers, is one of the most prized emblems in any of the services. It is never given; it is always earned and worn with pride.

Becoming qualified in submarines is not the end of a submarine sailor's education—it is the beginning. Submarines are complex scientific mechanisms,

Dry-land dive. The Askania diving trainer duplicates the diving controls of a waterborne submarine. Students operating this submarine simulator experience all the sensations of a dive at sea, and learn to cope with its problems.

and they demand special technical knowledge and skill on the part of the men who run them. The qualified submariner may return to the Submarine School for advanced training in a specialty, or he may go to one of many other Navy schools to continue his education.

To teach Navy men the latest applications of science to submarines, the Navy began operation of the Nuclear Power School in New London in January 1956. There submariners learn the theory and operation of nuclear reactors like those installed in *Nautilus, Seawolf,* and the atomic-powered submarines which follow them. At Nuclear Power School, a man receives instruction in mathematics, physics, reactor principles, thermodynamics, electrical theory, and nuclear power-plant systems. In addition, specialized training is given each man in his particular job aboard a nuclear-powered submarine.

In 1957, the Navy increased the number of men in the class at Nuclear Power School in order to have sufficient replacements for the numerous graduates of the school who are promoted to commissioned-officer rank.

For an officer, the path to becoming a submariner is longer and more difficult than for an enlisted man. The officer must first be qualified as a deck-watch officer aboard a surface ship before he requests assignment to submarines. And the officers' course at Submarine School is of six months' duration, instead of eight weeks.

At the School, the prospective submarine officer studies the theory and practice of handling submarines on the surface and submerged, and he is trained to be the diving officer of a submarine. The officer student also studies approach and attack tactics, the operation of the torpedo data computer, and periscope technique. He studies the mechanisms in torpedoes and makes them ready for firing, then he goes to sea in a submarine and fires at a target the torpedoes which he prepared. He learns the engineering and electrical machinery of submarines, and the theory and operation of radio, radar, and sonar equipment. At the end of six months, he has gained a thorough general knowledge of submarine matters.

When he graduates from Submarine School, the officer is ordered to duty on board a submarine. There, he applies the general knowledge acquired in Submarine School to learning about his new ship, for he is still not qualified in submarines. The unqualified officer prepares a notebook on various submarine subjects, such as engineering, communications, torpedoes and fire control, and tactics. He also learns how to handle the ship on the surface, how to dive and surface, how to conduct a torpedo attack, and how to operate the machinery and equipment on board.

When his commanding officer considers that the new officer has a thorough knowledge of submarine subjects and is competent to handle the ship, he recommends him for qualification in submarines. Acting on that recommendation the squadron commander forms a board of several qualified submarine officers to examine the officer candidate for qualification. The officers on the

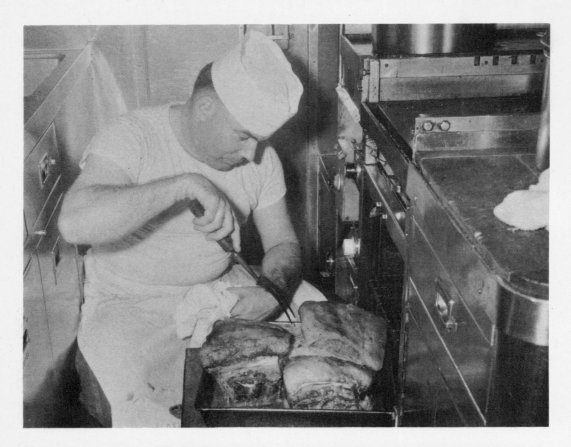

Submarines are famous for good food. Despite the limited galley area, submarine chefs serve the best meals in the United States Navy.

Silent battle of words beneath the sea. Off-duty crew members of the U.S.S. Albacore relax at the mess table by playing a word game.

board question the candidate on his knowledge of submarines and observe him put the submarine through its paces. When the members of the board are satisfied that they would like to have the officer serve with them as a qualified submariner, they recommend to the Chief of Naval Personnel that he be designated "Qualified in Submarines." Upon approval of the recommendation by the Chief of Naval Personnel, the officer is qualified and entitled to wear the gold dolphin insignia of the submarine service.

Qualification in submarines can be just the first step in the officer's education. He may go to Nuclear Power School, or Electronics School, or take postgraduate training in some field of special interest to him and of importance to the Navy.

After the submarine officer has completed two years of satisfactory service as a qualified officer, and has written an original thesis on a submarine subject, his commanding officer can recommend him for "Qualification to Command Submarines." That recommendation is passed up through the chain of command to the Chief of Naval Personnel, whose final approval is necessary to validate the command qualification. Although there is no special insignia to denote that he is qualified to command submarines, the official list of naval

A crew member ascends the ladder to the escape trunk during a routine drill. He does not require special breathing apparatus for free-buoyancy escape.

officers designates an officer with that qualification by placing the numeral "1" alongside his name.

At New London, Connecticut, and at Pearl Harbor, Hawaii, there are schools for prospective commanding officers of submarines. Called PCO School, the command course provides training in advanced submarine tactics and torpedo fire control. The course lasts for five weeks. Half of that time is devoted to studying advanced submarine tactics and related subjects, such as the tactical use of radar, sonar, and homing weapons. The remainder of the time, the officers go to sea in submarines and conduct exercises using the new methods and techniques they are learning.

While education and training are important in the making of a submariner, they would be of no value without men who are dedicated and determined to make the United States Navy's submarine service the finest in the world. There must be incentives to attract and keep such men, and, consequently, the advantages of the submarine service are many and varied. There are tangible advantages, such as the extra pay that submariners draw while serving on board an undersea craft and the good food that is served in submarines. Of perhaps more importance are the intangible but compelling advantages of

the submarine service. First, there is pride in being part of an elite corps, together with the comradeship that develops among men in such an outfit.
Then, there is a sense of accomplishment and satisfaction in doing a job that
is important. Also, there is each man's knowledge that his opportunity is limited solely by his own ability and desire. Unique in modern war, the submarine
operates deep in enemy territory—alone or with a few trusted companions,
like the Indian scout of frontier days. Hence, the submariner has more independence and latitude for individual action than can be found when operating with a large group.

Submariners are volunteers. The service they perform is demanding, sometimes uncomfortable, and downright dangerous, so there is no requirement
that men remain against their wishes—they may leave any time they like. But
men get a feeling of belonging in the informal, confident atmosphere that per-
vades the crew of a well-organized and well-run submarine. Few leave by
choice.

*Full complement. Nine submarines nest alongside the submarine tender U.S.S.
Nereus during a change of command ceremony for Submarine Squadron Five.
U.S.S.* Florikan, *submarine rescue vessel, is moored forward.*

12. The True Submarine—A New Force

AND NOW—the true submarine!

From Van Drebel's oar-propelled submersible to the high-speed snorkel submarines of the mid-twentieth century, designers of underwater ships had to accept one inescapable requirement—the need to return to the surface at frequent intervals in order to replenish the supply of air, an essential ingredient of prenuclear propulsive power. We have seen that whatever the prime source of power—whether human beings, steam boilers, Diesel engines, or the hydrogen-peroxide system—the generation of that power required oxygen. Electric batteries merely provided a means for storing a relatively small amount of energy originally produced by some oxygen-consuming prime source. In reality, the hydrogen-peroxide system involved the bulky, hazardous, short-lived stowage, in chemical compound, of a limited amount of oxygen.

On January 17, 1955, the submarine's release from its centuries-old dependence upon oxygen-supported combustion was signaled to the world in that historic message transmitted by U.S.S. *Nautilus:* "Underway on nuclear power." From that day on, submarines could be built to operate indefinitely beneath the surface. *Nautilus* made routine passages of more than 3,000 miles without coming up for air; she could, if necessary, have traveled submerged completely around the world. The implications of that new submarine capability constituted what Rear Admiral H. G. Rickover, nuclear power pioneer, called the "naval revolution." It forced a searching re-examination of national strategy—a new look which inevitably was to result in the rigorous displacement of vehicles and weapons which had but a few years before been regarded as ultimate instruments of victory in global war.

The propulsion innovation which brought about this naval revolution was a combination of something old and something new. The something old was steam, long a prime mover for man's power-generating machines. The something new was the controlled release of nuclear energy, which produced heat to make steam without using oxygen. The main engines of *Nautilus* were nothing new; they were conventional steam turbines like those which had driven high-speed ships since early in the twentieth century. It was the nuclear reactor which constituted the revolutionary feature of this potent new propulsion system.

The Manhattan District Engineers, builders of the world's first atomic bomb, commenced work on the development of a nuclear power plant in 1946. The following year, the Atomic Energy Commission, which succeeded the Manhattan Engineers, halted the work. However, shortly afterward, the Navy insisted that the development of a nuclear power plant for submarine propulsion was a pressing military requirement, and requested the Atomic Energy Commission to develop a reactor for that purpose. Finally, in 1949, at the Bettis Laboratory near Pittsburgh, Pennsylvania, active work started on the design of a pressurized-water type reactor to power a submarine.

In 1950, Congress authorized construction of the first nuclear-powered sub-

Hoisting her colors, the world's first true submarine, the nuclear-powered U.S.S. Nautilus, is commissioned into the United States Navy, September 1954.

marine. The initial step required the development and construction of a submarine thermal reactor at the National Reactor Testing Station, Arco, Idaho. From August 1950 until May 1953 that Mark I reactor was under design and construction, and in June 1953, after experimental activations, it performed a full-power run of long duration and was pronounced a success. The Mark I reactor never went to sea, but it served as the prototype for the Mark II reactor which was installed in *Nautilus*. Confidence in the outcome of the prototype reactor experiments was expressed by the laying of the keel of *Nautilus* in June 1952, a full year before the Mark I reactor had proved its capabilities.

The *Nautilus*-type reactor is called "thermal" because the nuclear reaction takes place in the low-velocity (thermal) energy range. When a neutron is absorbed by an atom of the uranium-235 isotope fuel, the nucleus of the uranium atom splits into pieces. The splitting-apart process is called fission, and the pieces are called fission fragments. The fragments travel at extremely high velocity, until they are stopped by surrounding material in the reactor. It is this stoppage which results in the production of heat, just as the impact of a bullet on a hard target generates heat. In addition to fission fragments, two or three neutrons fly off from each of the uranium nuclei which break apart. Some of these neutrons are absorbed into other uranium-235 nuclei, which repeat the fission process, causing a self-sustaining chain reaction and the continuous production of heat.

The reaction is regulated by the insertion of control rods into the reactor. These rods are made of hafnium, a metal which absorbs large quantities of neutrons. Thus, when the control rods are pushed in, many neutrons are absorbed in the hafnium and the reaction is slowed. When the rods are pulled out, neutrons are free to cause greater fission activity and the reaction is accelerated.

The heat generated by the fission process is used to raise the temperature of high-pressure water, called the primary coolant, which carries the heat from the reactor to a steam generator. The primary coolant is kept under high pressure to prevent its flashing into steam when heated, hence the reactor is referred to as a "pressurized-water" type.

In the steam generator, heat from the primary coolant water is transferred to low-pressure water, called feed water. The feed water, being under low pressure, boils and produces steam. The steam drives turbines which are geared to the propeller shafts. After the steam goes through the turbines, it passes to a condenser where it is cooled to water. That water, called condensate, is pumped back into the feed-water system and returned to the steam generator where it repeats its cycle.

While nuclear power freed the submarine's engines from the need for oxygen, it did not free the men in its crew from dependence on that vital element of the atmosphere. In the early years of underwater exploits, men who ventured down in primitive submarines often found themselves breathing air in which

"Underway on nuclear power." Fuel on board *U.S.S.* Nautilus *when she was commissioned propelled her for more than 60,000 miles The success of this ship's propulsion plant determined the design of later installations.*

"Emergency surface!" Breaking the surface at an extreme angle, the bow of nuclear-powered Nautilus *emerges from the sea. Normal surfacing is accomplished with a lesser inclination.*

the proportion of oxygen had become perilously small. It was soon discovered that even the hardiest submariner needs air in which oxygen comprises at least one part in six, in order to work efficiently during prolonged submergences. It is the amount of oxygen that the nuclear-propelled submarine can carry for air replenishment that limits the submerged endurance of the true submersible. The first atomic submarine carried sufficient oxygen, and supplementary equipment for cleansing the air of noxious gases, to support its crew for two hundred sixty-five hours. With the aid of electrochemistry, heat produced by the nuclear reactor can be used to extend the breathing time of the crew to practically indefinite limits, just as it has provided the true submarine with vastly extended cruising endurance. For oxygen is the main ingredient of sea water by weight and nuclear energy can be used to produce electric current, which can separate oxygen from water by electrolysis. Thus, oxygen made from the sea can provide an inexhaustible source for revitalizing the air inside the submarine.

The first nuclear-powered submarines were also limited in the time they could cruise completely submerged by their need to come to the surface in order to fix their position. Navigation necessitated an occasional return to shallow depth, so that a periscope or a radio antenna could be thrust above the surface. Thus exposed, the modern periscope can be used to take observations of celestial bodies, from which the navigator can determine the ship's position. A radio antenna can receive transmissions from shore-based electronic stations which permit the navigator to fix his position thousands of miles at sea, even with an overcast obscuring the sky.

But by 1958, the end of this dependence upon external aids to submerged navigation was in sight. The development of Ships Inertial Navigation System was nearing the point where any ship, including a submarine, could navigate accurately for long periods of time without the aid of celestial observations or shore-based electronic transmissions. The Inertial Navigation System is designed to keep a record of a ship's position at all times, in much the same way that an inertial guidance system directs a long-range missile to its target—by finely balanced instruments. In addition, progress in accurate charting of the mountains and valleys of the ocean floor gave the submarine commander better pictures of those submerged topographical features which, scanned by the fathometer, could give him a means of fixing the ship's position without coming to the surface.

In April 1956, for example, *Nautilus* made a deep high-speed transit from Key West, Florida, to New London, Connecticut, navigating by means of the contours of the bottom off the Atlantic seaboard. The navigator accurately fixed the ship's position while passing over a 500-fathom depth in the Hudson River Canyon, only one minute off his estimated time.

As long as the conventional submarine had to carry duplicate power plants —one for use while submerged and another for use on the surface—it required an engineering feat of the first magnitude to cram adequate power capability

Crewmen aboard the U.S.S. Nautilus *do their laundry the easy way. The ship's modern washing machine is a far cry from the salt-water bucket of earlier days.*

into either of those plants. The craft was inevitably underpowered. But nuclear power at last provided a source that could be used either surfaced or submerged. *With that new power, the true submarine could be driven faster under water than on the surface.* A modern 4,000-ton destroyer, thrusting its lean hull through the seas at 30 knots, plows up a bow wave romantically known as a "bone in her teeth." That bow wave delights the eyes of true sailors. It is beautiful, but costly; it consumes 60 per cent of the 50,000 horsepower needed to propel the ship at that speed. In contrast to the destroyer, a deeply submerged 4,000-ton submarine can be driven at 30 knots with less than 20,000 horsepower. The main difference is that the submarine at deep submergence makes no surface waves, so that the power saved by not "carrying a bone in her teeth" goes into making the submarine go faster.

Nautilus and the four Skate-class submarines, the first generation of nuclear-powered undersea craft, were conservative in design. Admiral Rickover referred to the *Nautilus*-type power plant as the "Kitty Hawk model"—a pioneer design to be succeeded by more powerful, advanced types as development progressed. In 1958, *Skipjack,* with a nuclear power plant calculated to drive her *Albacore*-type hull to a new submerged speed record, was under construction; and the keel was laid for *Triton,* with a two-reactor power plant designed to thrust her giant body through the water at high speed. The technologi-

The newest shape in underwater travel. U.S.S. Skipjack *has a nuclear power plant designed to drive her streamlined hull to a new submerged speed record.*

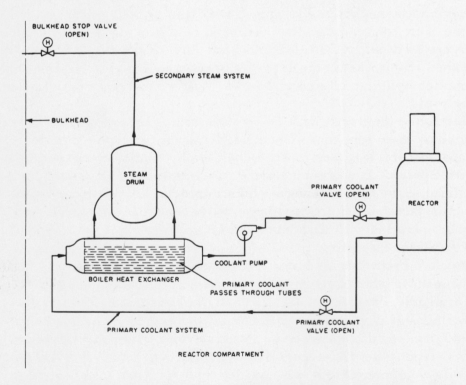

Diagram of reactor compartment of a nuclear-powered submarine, showing pressurized water reactor, primary coolant flow, and boiler heat exchanger (steam generator). Steam in the secondary steam system is taken off to drive turbines which are geared to the propeller shafts.

cal revolution that follows a breakthrough of major significance had already begun.

The advent of nuclear power has provided engineers with a new challenge: the development of means of transforming vast amounts of available heat into useful power, and the effective application of that power to propel a submarine. Gone was the day when a major problem was the development of enough heat to provide the power desired for greater speed and range. Today's engineer is confronted with an embarrassment of riches—he has a means of generating within a small space more heat than he can handle with present methods of transfer and propulsion. Steam turbines and the screw propeller have reached the utmost limits of their effectiveness under the impact of atomic energy.

The first step in converting heat to useful propulsive power involves its transmission from the reactor. That is the function of the primary coolant which, in the *Nautilus*-type reactor, is water. Water has been very successful in transferring heat from fires fueled by wood, coal, or oil, for it could carry away most of the heat that such fuels could generate. But when atomic fuels came on the scene, water was no longer capable of handling the vast quantity of heat made available by a reactor. The advantages of nuclear power for submarines were so great, and the need for capitalizing on them so urgent, that engineers used old, reliable water in the *Nautilus* power plant even though they knew that it was not the most efficient means of solving the problem. Even at less than optimum efficiency, *Nautilus* was the most powerful undersea craft in the world.

Meanwhile the search for a better coolant was pressed. It was known that metals and gases were both more efficient than water for the purpose. A metal coolant, sodium, was used in the second nuclear submarine power plant, installed in *Seawolf*. It was not a complete success, however, because a small leak developed in the heat-exchanger while running at full power, a serious matter due to the fact that sodium becomes some 30,000 times as radioactive as water. Further operation with that leak would have resulted in the escape of radioactive sodium into other parts of the system, so the defective section was blocked off. From then on, *Seawolf* operated her power plant at reduced output; but she was still capable of making 90 per cent of designed speed.

Fortunately, discovery of the defect in the *Seawolf* plant did not disrupt the Navy's nuclear-powered submarine building program. The need for the best new submarines that could be built was obvious, and with the success of the *Nautilus*-type power plant the Navy made plans to put water-cooled reactors in all new submarines. It was decided that until the problem of a highly radioactive coolant was solved, no more sodium-cooled reactors would be built for submarines.

While more submarines using pressurized-water type reactors were being built, engineers pressed the search for a better means of converting heat from nuclear fission into power. The success of the search in turn required progress in another field, that of converting increased power into thrust for propelling the submarine. Twin-screw propellers, which transmitted the thousands of horsepower of *Nautilus'* turbines to the water, were adequate for the task. However, in the design of the more-powerful *Skipjack,* engineers changed over to a large, single propeller, fitted at the end of her finely tapered stern—a design already proved efficient in the experimental high-speed *Albacore.* To transmit still more power to the water, another propeller, rotating in the opposite direction, can be fitted to the shaft—a principle previously used in aircraft to apply the increased power of modern engines. Counterrotating propellers will drive submarines up to about 50 knots, but after that jet propulsion will take over just as it did in aircraft.

Even when the problems of transmitting fission energy are solved, engineers cannot rest on their laurels. Already scientists are working toward a new source of heat, harnessing the tremendous energy of nuclear fusion. When means have been developed to control the heat generated by nuclear fusion, the virtually limitless power of the hydrogen-bomb type reaction will be available to increase the performance of the submarine's engines in a dramatic advance comparable to the controlled atom-bomb type reaction replacing the Diesel engine.

What, then, is the military significance of this true submarine? It has potentially greater speed than any other type of ship; it has the ability to operate submerged for prolonged periods of time and to traverse immense distances; and, of utmost importance, it can operate with almost complete immunity from detection, a characteristic possessed by no other vehicle on the land, on the surface of the seas, or in the air. It can carry and fire the most advanced missiles of the present or the foreseeable future.

By 1957, the United States Navy had acquired valuable experience with submarine-launched missiles, using winged, air-breathing Regulus missiles fired from the veteran *Tunny* and *Barbero.* The new *Grayback* was commissioned March 7, 1958, while *Growler* and the nuclear-powered *Halibut,* all designed to launch Regulus missiles, were under construction. The missile-firing submarine fleet was on the verge of becoming a force to be reckoned with.

While the Regulus missiles are potent and versatile weapons, they cannot be launched from underwater. To use them, the submarine must surface and expose itself to detection from radar beams which can sweep and illuminate the surface of the sea day and night. So plans were made to develop a missile that could be fired from below the surface, and in January 1957, it was announced that such a weapon was well along in development. That weapon is Polaris, a 1,500-mile-range ballistic missile designed especially for shipboard use. It uses solid fuel. Since the solid propellant grain is carried inside the missile at all times, no time need be wasted in fueling the weapon before fir-

The first missile-firing submarine joined the Navy with the commissioning of U.S.S. Grayback, March 7, 1958. She is armed with the Regulus II guided missile.

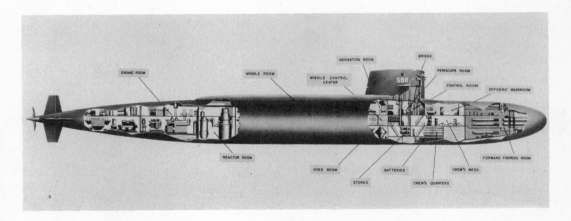

ENGINE ROOM

MISSILE ROOM

NAVIGATION ROOM

BRIDGE

MISSILE CONTROL CENTER

PERISCOPE ROOM

CONTROL ROOM

OFFICERS' WARDROOM

REACTOR ROOM

GYRO ROOM

STORES

BATTERIES

CREW'S QUARTERS

CREW'S MESS

FORWARD TORPEDO ROOM

Fleet ballistic-missile submarine. This submarine has been especially designed to fire the Polaris missile from below the surface of the sea.

ing. It is smaller and lighter than liquid-fuel missiles of comparable range. And since there is no volatile liquid oxygen or fuel to store and pump, the solid-fuel missile is safer to handle aboard ship.

The smaller size of Polaris carries with it another advantage: a submarine of a given size can pack more missiles. The number of missiles to be carried in the first Polaris submarines is far greater than would have been possible with liquid-fuel missiles.

Early in the research program, naval officers and civilian scientists analyzed the Polaris system—the submarine, its nuclear power plant and its weapons—and found that the first submarines should be designed to carry between ten and twenty Polaris missiles. To carry fewer would mean that more submarines would be required to constitute a sizable deterrent force. To carry more would mean that the submarines would sacrifice too much speed and maneuverability. In addition, putting too many eggs in one basket would restrict the number of submarines employed—it would make the enemy's defense problem somewhat simpler.

In 1958, although the Polaris missile had not been fired as a complete unit,

"Operation Pop-up." Up from the depths soars a Polaris test missile. Underwater launching tests lead to the perfection of the Navy's subsurface launching techniques.

test vehicles had been launched successfully and component tests had indicated that the complete missile would be ready by 1960.

In addition to carrying 1,500-mile-range missiles, Polaris submarines will be equipped with sonar and torpedo tubes like other submarines. Thus, while patrolling quietly in remote ocean areas, waiting for the signal to launch their long-range weapons, they will serve as outposts of the sea-borne forces guarding the approaches to our shores. Their greatest service may be spent in this secondary role, for their very existence will contribute to the prevention of any situation demanding the unleashing of their primary weapons.

The implications are as dramatic as they are inescapable. No target, be it aircraft, ship, or land installation, is beyond the attack reach of the fully developed nuclear-powered submarine. What its torpedoes cannot reach and destroy, its missiles can seek out and devastate. The true submarine, like the fast surface task force with its missile and air power, possesses the mobility that makes it virtually immune from land-based ballistic missiles. The true submarine is endowed with the additional capability of concealment that enables it to evade almost any kind of attack. Only another true submarine can

An artist's conception of the Polaris-carrying submarine. Nuclear-powered, it will be capable of remaining on station undetected for long periods of time.

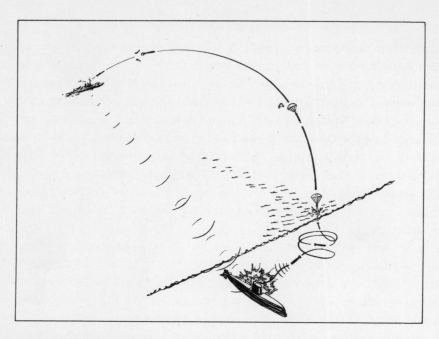

The "RAT" Attack. When the destroyer's sonar has detected the submarine, a fire-control system trains and elevates the "RAT" launcher, setting the range. In the air the rocket-propelled torpedo is retarded by parachute. When it goes beneath the surface, the torpedo separates from the rocket and begins a search pattern, pursuing the target by sound signals until it makes contact.

battle it on even terms. To the nation which maintains the leading position in the infinitely mobile striking forces of the sea will go the power to deter war or to determine its outcome. The Soviet Union is reported to have made trials of an atomic-powered submarine and to have started a building program of such craft.

Consider the threat posed by a force of nuclear-powered guided missile submarines. They can select times and places of their own choosing from which to launch attacks against any places within the borders of the enemy nation. With modern aids to navigation and the most advanced forms of missiles, capable of being launched from beneath the surface, the true submarine can launch its attack without ever revealing itself.

What is the best means of avoiding the destruction of which this craft is capable? Strategically, it would appear to be attainment, by a nation dedicated to peace, of dominance in nuclear submarine strength. In the hands of such a nation the true submarine is the true war deterrent. That warship of potentially terrible destruction may be the ultimate factor which will prevent catastrophic war. Tactically, the defense against the missile-armed, nuclear submarine is the most difficult problem confronting defense policy makers and scientists. Even an antimissile missile, effective against long-range weapons launched from fixed bases, could not be guaranteed to stop short time-of-flight missiles launched from mobile sea-borne bases. To stop the submarine before it strikes requires detection, location, identification, and destruction. An invention in underwater detection comparable to the advance made by radar in surface detection would provide the scientific breakthrough on which to base an advanced antisubmarine system. The detection equipment would be combined with modern weapons, including homing torpedoes, rockets, or atomic depth charges. Forces capable of delivering those weapons within lethal range of the enemy before he reaches his firing position would complete the system. Specially designed antisubmarine submarines could be major components of those forces.

Even in the event of a "conventional war"—one in which, presumably, nuclear weapons of massive destruction would not be employed—the submarine looms as a decisive factor. In such a war, conventional tactics, conventional weapons, and conventional means of transportation would be major elements of the war-making capability of opposing forces. In light of the stark reality that no nation is today independent of sources of essential materials which must come from across the seas, the submarine emerges as the means by which use of the seas can be reserved to one side and denied to the other. Its capability to run down and destroy surface targets makes it the prime means of slashing the ocean supply lines of an opponent. At the same time, its almost complete freedom from detection emphasizes its own potential as an unseverable line of supply to that nation which has the foresight to exploit the true submarine as a cargo carrier.

As new record piled on new record, *Nautilus* continued to demonstrate the unique capability and far-reaching implications of the atomic dimension in undersea travel. On August 8, 1958, President Eisenhower dramatically announced that the first atomic-powered submarine had crossed the top of the world by sailing submerged from the Pacific to the Atlantic by way of the North Pole. Under the command of Commander William R. Anderson, U.S.N., the submarine and her crew of one hundred and sixteen officers and men sailed from Honolulu on July 23, for the announced purpose of conducting another series of prolonged submergence tests. How prolonged those tests were to be was not revealed until the White House announcement was made. The voyage terminated at Portland, England, some 8,146 nautical miles from Honolulu, on August 12. It had been made in nineteen days at an average speed of 17 knots, despite the fact that the ship had necessarily proceeded with some caution in the polar waters through which man had never before sailed. Although the top speed of the *Nautilus* was not revealed by the Navy, Commander Anderson stated publicly that he had crossed the Pole at "more than twenty knots."

Of technical interest were certain items of equipment installed in *Nautilus*

Commander William R. Anderson, U.S.N., (left) and Commander James F. Calvert, U.S.N., (right), the captains of Nautilus *and* Skate *respectively when these two nuclear submarines first passed beneath the North Pole.*

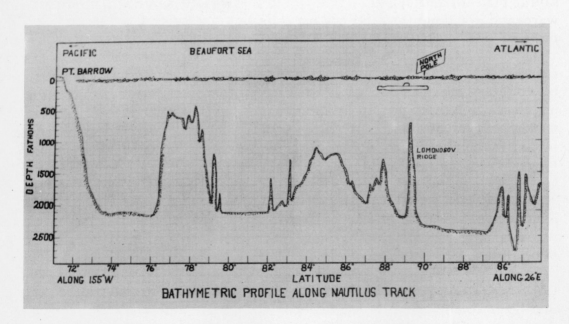

Depth soundings taken by Nautilus *in August 1958 reveal the contours of the ocean bed beneath the polar icecap. This was the first time such scientific information could be obtained in this way.*

for her historic cruise. Ten separate sound devices for detecting obstacles in her path and three for measuring the depth of the ocean floor aided her navigator in picking his way cautiously through the ice-covered reaches. As an additional aid to safe navigation and scientific study, *Nautilus* was equipped with a television camera which projected on a screen inside the ship a continuous image of the underside of the ice fields beneath which she sailed. Taking advantage of the information developed by *Nautilus,* U.S.S. *Skate* under Commander James F. Calvert, crossed the North Pole under the ice on August 11, 1958.

Aside from the mass of new scientific data collected on the voyage, *Nautilus'* feat kindled the imagination of shipping men all over the world. Mindful of the steps already being taken to develop commercial cargo submarines of huge displacement, they saw in the polar cruise dramatic proof that peaceful shipping could now choose any waters of the earth, even those covered with ice, for the most speedy and economical routes between the trade centers of the world.

To military strategists, the voyage emphasized the threat to any enemy offered by Polaris-type missiles fired from nuclear submarines hidden beneath the polar icecap. Equally obvious were the opportunities for greater concealment thus offered to the submarine. Almost impossible to intercept in the open sea by the most advanced detecting gear available, the nuclear submarine, sailing beneath a shield of ice that would reflect both sound and electronic waves and would bar the use of surface antisubmarine fighters, posed a defense problem for which no publicly announced solution was immediately available.

The war potential of the submarine is naturally the characteristic of this nuclear-age creation foremost in the minds of almost everyone. But if, as we believe, the submarine may become in our hands one of the means of preventing nuclear war, then perhaps its peacetime potential will be realized. Today, no means of transportation, whether on the land, on the surface of the sea, or in the air, is independent of the vagaries of weather. Storms slow and sometimes stop all of them. But for the true submarine, there are no storms. Gliding smoothly in the depths below the regions of atmospheric disturbances and wind-lashed waves, traveling at speeds which may one day be measured in hundreds of miles per hour, it will provide the ultimate in comfort, punctuality, and safety. No more seasickness. No more airsickness. Truly a new era in transoceanic travel!

In 1958, the nuclear-age submarine held the promise of helping to preserve the peace, and revealed a new concept for the peaceful use of the true submarine as a more efficient means for communication and exchange between the peoples of the world. The fulfillment of that promise depends in part upon the attainment of a commanding lead in nuclear-powered submarines by a nation dedicated to peace. Through the genius of its scientists and engineers and the vision of its naval planners, the United States gained a head start in the nuclear submarine race.

Time will tell if that head start will assist in the lasting predominance that could bring the blessings of peace and security to the free world, and a better way of life to all mankind.

U.S.S. Skipjack *being launched at Groton, Connecticut. The first submarine to combine the advantages of nuclear power, such as* Nautilus *utilizes, with the shark-shaped hull of* Albacore, Skipjack *obtains additional maneuverability and speed from her single propeller and from the use of sail diving planes, or "underwater wings."*

Index

Figures in italics indicate illustrations

157

ABOUT THE AUTHORS

COMMANDER CHARLES W. RUSH, JR., was graduated from Annapolis in 1941. After service in destroyers, he entered submarines and made war patrols in the Pacific in *Thresher* and *Billfish*. He took postgraduate training in missiles after the war and received the degree of Aeronautical Engineer from the California Institute of Technology, then served as executive officer of the submarine *Carbonero*, which was fitted to launch and guide missiles. Commander Rush later commanded the submarines *Queenfish* and *Blackfin*, after which he became officer-in-charge of the Submarine Prospective Commanding Officers' School at Pearl Harbor. He has also been Head of the Submarine Weapons Systems Section in the Office of the Chief of Naval Operations.

W. C. CHAMBLISS began his career as a newspaperman in New York in 1924. In 1930, he became a Naval Aviator. During World War II, he served in the Pacific and was aboard the aircraft carrier *Wasp* when that ship was sunk by enemy submarine action during the Guadalcanal Campaign. He has also served in Naval Forces, Eastern Atlantic and Mediterranean, in the Pacific Northwest, and in Washington. He is the author of three books, numerous short stories and articles, and is a member of the New York Bar.

COMMANDER HERBERT J. GIMPEL enlisted in the V-7 Program of the Navy in 1942 and was commissioned in the United States Naval Reserve. Following his training, he served in the aircraft carrier *Bataan*, participating in the Third and Fifth Fleet raids in support of the Okinawa assault and the operations against Japan. Since the war Commander Gimpel has served as Public Information Officer to Commander Destroyer Force, U. S. Atlantic Fleet, and as Historian for Allied Forces Southern Europe at Naples, Italy. He has served in several posts in Washington, most recently as Head of the Magazine and Book Branch in the Navy's Office of Information.

PHOTO AND ILLUSTRATION CREDITS